NEW 2018

by **ARGO**
BROTHERS

COMMON CORE
MATH

GRADE 5

PART II: FREE RESPONSE

Visit **www.argoprep.com** to get
FREE access to our online platform.

ARGOPREP.COM

Welcome to **ARGO PREP!**

You have successfully unlocked the magical properties of your workbook and can now access full video explanations to each of our math and english workbooks.

Please **select the subject** that you would like to have explantions for.

LEARN ENGLISH   **LEARN MATH**

1000+ Minutes of Video Explanations and more!

Authors: Kellie Zimmer
                    Anayet Chowdhury
                    Eduard Suleyman
                    Vladislav Suleyman

Design: Vladislav Suleyman

At Argo Brothers, we are dedicated to providing quality and effective supplemental practice for your child. We would love to hear your honest feedback and **review** of our workbooks on **Amazon**.

Argo Brothers is one of the leading providers of supplemental educational products and services. We offer affordable and effective test prep solutions to educators, parents and students. Learning should be fun and easy! For that reason, most of our workbooks come with detailed video answer explanations taught by one of our fabulous instructors. Our goal is to make your life easier, so let us know how we can help you by e-mailing us at **info@argobrothers.com**.

OTHER BOOKS BY ARGO BROTHERS

Here are some other test prep workbooks by Argo Brothers you may be interested in. All of our workbooks come equipped with detailed video explanations to make your learning experience a breeze! Subscribe to our mailing list at www.argobrothers.com to receive custom updates about your education.

GRADE 2

GRADE 3

GRADE 4
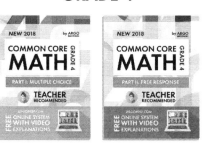

GRADE 5
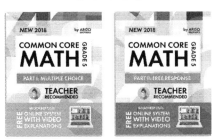

GRADE 6

GRADE 7

GRADE 4

GRADE 5

TABLE OF
CONTENTS

HOW TO USE
THE BOOK

This workbook is designed to give lots of practice with the math Common Core State Standards (CCSS). By practicing and mastering this entire workbook, your child will become very familiar and comfortable with the state math exam. If you are a teacher using this workbook for your students, you will notice each question is labeled with the specific standard so you can easily assign your students problems in the workbook. This workbook takes the CCSS and divides them up among 20 weeks. By working on these problems on a daily basis, students will be able to (1) find any deficiencies in their understanding and/or practice of math and (2) have small successes each day that will build proficiency and confidence in their abilities.

You can find detailed video explanations to each problem in the book by visiting:
www.argoprep.com

We strongly recommend watching the videos as it will reinforce the fundamental concepts. Please note, scrap paper may be necessary while using this workbook so that the student has sufficient space to show their work.

For a detailed overview of the Common Core State Standards for 5th grade, please visit:
www.corestandards.org/Math/Content/5/introduction/

For more practice with 5th Grade Math, be sure to check out our other book, Common Core Math Workbook Grade 5: Multiple Choice

Congratulations on choosing to work at becoming a better math student! It starts here with Week 1 where you will learn about how digits have different values according to their location in a number.

You can find detailed video explanations to each problem in the book by visiting:
ArgoPrep.com

Digits that lie to the right of other digits within the same number are smaller than the digit on the left. The 4 in 48 is 10 times the size of the 4 in 94.

---

1. How many times greater is the value of (A) the digit 3 in 75,308 than the value of the digit 3 in 49,735? (B) the digit 7 in the two numbers?

5.NBT.1

---

2. The digit 8 in 104,682 is _30_ times the value of the 8 in 35,807.

5.NBT.1

---

3. Write 2 numbers.

   A. One number should have only one 6 in which that 6 has a value that is $\frac{1}{100}$ the value of the 6 in 96,514.
   B. One number should have only one 6 that has a value that is 10 times the value of the 6 in 3,649.

5.NBT.1

---

4. The number 62.098 is given. In a different number, the 2 represents a value which is one-tenth of the value of the 2 in 62.098. What value is represented by the 2 in the other number?

5.NBT.1

---

5. The digit 6 in 524,681 is _____ times the value of the 6 in 68,390.

5.NBT.1

---

6. How many times greater is the value of the digit 9 in 3,917 than the value of the digit 9 in 84,019?

5.NBT.1

TIP of the DAY

If the same digit is in the tens and hundreds places, the digit in the tens place is $\frac{1}{10}$ the value of that same digit in the hundreds place. Example 50 is 10 times greater than 5.

---

1. Write a number that has only one 3 and where that 3 has a value that is $\frac{1}{10}$ the value of the 3 in 39,462.

5.NBT.1

---

2. How many times is the value of the digit 3 in 81,302 than the value of the digit 3 in 37,415?

5.NBT.1

The table below shows the number of visitors to a sports arena on certain days. Use the table to answer questions 3 – 5.

Tuesday	54,260
Wednesday	47,835
Friday	91,672
Sunday	105,483

---

3. Which day has a 4 that is 100 times the value of the 4 in 12,364?

5.NBT.1

---

4. Which day has a 7 that is $\frac{1}{10}$ the value of the 7 in 8,725?

5.NBT.1

---

5. Which day has a 5 that is $\frac{1}{100}$ the value of the 5 in 91,564?

5.NBT.1

 **DAY 3**

If the same digit is in the tens and thousands places, the digit in the thousands place is 100 times the value of that same digit in the tens place. Example: 4000 is 100 times greater than 40.

 **TIP** of the **DAY**

---

1. The number 3954.76 is given. In a different number, the 7 represents a value which is one-tenth of the value of the 7 in 3954.76. What value is represented by the 7 in the other number?

5.NBT.1

---

2. The digit 9 in 7,691 is _____ times the value of the 9 in 19,348.

5.NBT.1

---

3. How many times greater is the value of the digit 1 in 81,465 than the value of the digit 1 in 67,821?

5.NBT.1

---

4. Which term can be put in the blank to make the statement true?

$$800,000 = 80 \underline{\hspace{3cm}}$$

5.NBT.1

---

5. Write 2 numbers.

A. One number should have only one 5 in which that 5 has a value that is $\frac{1}{10}$ the value of the 5 in 27,519.

B. One number should have only one 5 that has a value that is 100 times the value of the 5 in 45,628.

5.NBT.1

---

6. The digit 3 in 3,420,517 is _____ times the value of the 3 in 630,210.

5.NBT.1

---

1. The digit 7 in 521,674 is _____ times the value of the 1 in 195,837.

5.NBT.1

---

2. Which place value can be put in the blank to make the statement true?

$$6,500,000 = 65 \underline{\hspace{4cm}}$$

5.NBT.1

---

3. What is the product of 13.76 and (A) 10, (B) 100, and (C) 1000?

5.NBT.2

---

4. Write 23×10^4 in standard form.

5.NBT.2

---

5. What is the quotient when 349.16 is divided by (A) 10, (B) 100, and (C) 1000?

5.NBT.2

---

6. Using powers of 10 and exponents only, write an expression that is equivalent to (A) 100,000 and (B) 100.

5.NBT.2

 # DAY 5: ASSESSMENT

1. The digit 1 in 780,159 is _____ times the value of the 1 in 31,457.

5.NBT.1

2. Which place value can be put in the blank to make the statement true?

$$2,000,000 = 20 \underline{\hspace{4cm}}$$

5.NBT.1

3. What is 0.0419 × 1,000?

5.NBT.2

4. What is the product of 734.508 and (A) 100, (B) 1,000 (C) 100,000?

5.NBT.2

5. Write 7×10^6 in standard form.

5.NBT.2

6. What is the quotient when 12.769 is divided by (A) 100, (B) 1,000 and (C) 10,000?

5.NBT.2

7. Write a number that has an 8 with a value that is $\dfrac{1}{100}$ the value of the 8 in 786,152.

5.NBT.1

 # DAY 6
CHALLENGE QUESTION

A. What is 13,689.4 when multiplied by 100 and 10,000?

B. What is 13,689.4 when it is divided by 100 and 10,000?

5.NBT.2

In Week 2, you will practice writing numbers in different ways - in expanded form, in words, and in standard form.

You can find detailed video explanations to each problem in the book by visiting: ArgoPrep.com

 **DAY 1**

The exponent on a power of 10 indicates how many zeroes follow the 1. Examples: 10^5 has 5 zeroes, or 100,000 and 10^2 has 2 zeroes and equals 100.

 **TIP** of the **DAY**

---

1. Write 92×10^3 in standard form.

5.NBT.2

---

2. What is the product of 18.03 and (A) 10? (B) 1,000?

5.NBT.2

---

3. What is 4×10^2 in standard form?

5.NBT.2

---

4. Which term can be put in the blank to make the statement true?

$$3,000 = 30 \underline{\hspace{3cm}}$$

5.NBT.1

---

5. What is 651.29 divided by (A) 10,000? (B) 100?

5.NBT.2

---

6. Write 9.04×10^2 in standard form.

5.NBT.2

TIP of the **DAY** | 90 tens is the same as 900 and 90 hundred thousands is 9,000,000. | # DAY 2

---

1. Which term can be put in the blank to make the statement true?

$$8,500,000 = 85 \rule{3cm}{0.4pt}$$

5.NBT.1

---

2. What is 15,928 divided by 10^2?

5.NBT.2

---

3. Write a number that is $\dfrac{1}{10}$ of the value of: $9(100,000) + 5(10,000) + 6(1,000) + 8(100) + 1(10) + 2\left(\dfrac{1}{10}\right) + 5\left(\dfrac{1}{100}\right)$

5.NBT.3

---

4. Write thirty-one hundred ten and eight hundredths in (A) standard form and (B) expanded form.

5.NBT.3

---

5. Write 354.109 in (A) expanded form and (B) in words.

5.NBT.3

---

6. Write a number sentence using a comparison symbol, 0.12 and 12 hundreds.

5.NBT.3

 **DAY 3**

The word "and" means the whole numbers are finished and you're moving onto decimal numbers. Four and five tenths is 4 and $\frac{5}{10}$ or 4.5.

 **TIP** of the **DAY**

---

1. What is 17,892.1 written (A) in words and (B) in expanded form?

5.NBT.3

---

2. Which expression is equivalent to 2×10^4?

5.NBT.2

---

3. Place the following numbers in order from smallest to largest:

86.7   86.79   86.97   86.94

5.NBT.3

---

4. What number is one-tenth of the expanded form below?

$$5(10,000) + 3(1,000) + 7(100) + 6(1) + 2\left(\frac{1}{100}\right)$$

5.NBT.3

---

5. Write seven thousand fourteen and two hundredths in (A) standard form and (B) expanded form.

5.NBT.3

---

6. Look at 74.382. In a different number, the 8 represents a value which is one-tenth of the value of the 8 in 74.382. What value is represented by the 8 in the other number?

5.NBT.1

TIP of the **DAY** — A place value ending in "ths" means it is a number to the right of the decimal point.

 **DAY 4**

---

1. Write 360.281 in (A) words and in (B) expanded form.

5.NBT.3

---

2. What number is one hundredth of the expanded form below?

$$7(1,000) + 9(100) + 2(10) + 5(1) + 4\left(\frac{1}{10}\right) + 3\left(\frac{1}{100}\right)$$

5.NBT.3

---

3. Place the following numbers in order from smallest to largest:

314.807   314.9   313.975   314.78

5.NBT.3

---

4. Write sixteen thousand, two hundred nine and twelve hundredths in (A) standard form and (B) expanded form.

5.NBT.3

---

5. Write a number sentence using a comparison symbol, 17.9 and 17.869.

5.NBT.3

---

6. Place the following numbers in order from smallest to largest:

6.107   6.2   6.14   6.143

5.NBT.3

17

 # DAY 5: ASSESSMENT

1. The number 29.41 is given. In a different number, the 4 represents a value which is one-tenth of the value of the 4 in 29.41. What value is represented by the 4 in the other number?

5.NBT.1

2. What number is one-tenth of the expanded form below?

$$5(1,000) + 6(100) + 3(10) + 8(1) + 4\left(\frac{1}{100}\right) + 2\left(\frac{1}{1000}\right)$$

5.NBT.3

3. Place the following numbers in order from smallest to largest:

241.68   240.999   241.7   241.705

5.NBT.3

4. Write four hundred thousand, eight hundred twenty-six and five thousandths in (A) standard form and (B) expanded form.

5.NBT.3

5. Write a number sentence using a comparison symbol, 35.8 and 35.800.

5.NBT.3

6. Place the following numbers in order from smallest to largest:

726.9   726.875   726.91   726.95

5.NBT.3

 # DAY 6

CHALLENGE QUESTION

Write 8,907,145.26 in (A) words and (B) in expanded form.

5.NBT.3

Week 3 will allow you to practice rounding numbers, even decimal numbers! You will also use multiplication for many of the questions.

You can find detailed video explanations to each problem in the book by visiting:
ArgoPrep.com

DAY 1

For rounding, look at the digit to the right of the place you are rounding to. If it is a five or greater, the number rounds up.

TIP of the DAY

---

1. Gas was $2.9154 per gallon. Round 2.9154 to the nearest (A) tenth, (B) hundredth and (C) thousandth.

5.NBT.4

---

2. What is 22 − 0.76?

5.NBT.4

---

3. Write a number that has a 9 that is $\frac{1}{10}$ the value of the 9 in 7.593.

5.NBT.1

---

4. Round 784.39 to the nearest (A) tenth and (B) hundred.

5.NBT.4

---

5. What is 3×10^3 in standard form?

5.NBT.2

---

6. 84.719 + 210 = ?

5.NBT.4

TIP of the **DAY** | Recall a whole number like 37 has a decimal point after the 7 and can be written as 37 or 37.0.

DAY 2

The table below shows the lengths of 4 pipes in inches. Use the table to answer questions 1 – 3.

Pipe A	182.37
Pipe B	182.34
Pipe C	182.4
Pipe D	181.99

1. If the pipes were laid end-to-end, what would their distance be?

5.NBT.5

2. Place the pipes in order from shortest to longest.

5.NBT.3

3. Write a number sentence using the lengths of Pipes A and C.

5.NBT.3

4. What is 4,506.3892 rounded to the nearest (A) tenth? (B) thousandth?

5.NBT.4

5. What is 261.98 + 4,082.7?

5.NBT.5

DAY 3

When multiplying by a power of 10, the decimal moves to the right the same number of places as there are zeroes in the power of 10.

1. Find the product of 17 and 92.

5.NBT.5

2. What is 5,973 × 21?

5.NBT.5

The table below shows Alan's monthly expenses. Use it to answer questions 3 – 4.

Rent	$1,375
Cable/Phone	$458
Electricity	$296

3. If Alan paid for 3 months of each of his expenses, what would he pay for (A) rent? (B) cable/phone and (C) electricity?

5.NBT.5

4. What are Alan's total expenses for 1 year?

5.NBT.5

5. If you are dividing a number by 10^6, what direction do you move the decimal point and how many places?

5.NBT.2

 of the DAY

When dividing by a power of 10, the decimal moves to the left the same number of places as there are zeroes in the power of 10.

DAY 4

1. What is the product of 4,902 and 286?

5.NBT.5

2. What is 925.8 – 39.17?

5.NBT.4

3. The digit 5 in 75,091 is _____ times the value of the 5 in 98,350.

5.NBT.1

4. Find: 3,068 × 205

5.NBT.5

5. What is 587.06 divided by 10^2?

5.NBT.2

6. What is the product of 297 and 6,851?

5.NBT.5

 # DAY 5: ASSESSMENT

1. What is the sum of 871.92 and 207.6?

5.NBT.5

2. What is 914.9971 rounded to the nearest (A) tenth (B) hundredth (C) thousandth?

5.NBT.4

3. What is 5,689,513 rounded to the nearest (A) hundred? (B) thousand? (C) hundred thousand?

5.NBT.4

4. What is the product of 4,768 and 100?

5.NBT.5

5. Write 942.51 in (A) words and (B) expanded form.

5.NBT.3

6. What is 5,170 × 62?

5.NBT.5

 # DAY 6

CHALLENGE QUESTION

Round 5,618.98 to the nearest (A) tenth and (B) hundred. Add those 2 rounded numbers together. What is the sum?

5.NBT.4

24

Week 4 has lots of decimals. Be sure to line up the decimals when adding or subtracting and count decimals when multiplying.

You can find detailed video explanations to each problem in the book by visiting:
ArgoPrep.com

1. Write an equation that could be modeled below.

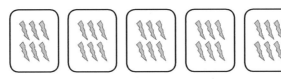

5.NBT.6

2. What is the quotient when 5,532 is divided by 12?

5.NBT.6

3. Find: 7704 ÷ 36 = ?

5.NBT.6

4. What is the value of the expression below?

$$8514 \div 22$$

5.NBT.6

5. How many times greater is the value of the digit 7 in 379,501 than the value of the digit 7 in 83,712?

5.NBT.1

6. What equation could be shown by the model below?

5.NBT.6

When working with numbers, it is a good idea to check your answers by rounding the original problem to see if your answers are reasonable.

DAY 2

---

1. There are 11 shelves that contain and 5,676 rolls of tape. How many rolls are on each shelf?

5.NBT.6

---

2. What is the value of the expression below?

$$4455 \div 45$$

5.NBT.6

---

3. Which equation is shown in the model below?

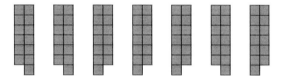

5.NBT.6

---

4. The number 81.794 is given. In a different number, the 1 represents a value which is one-tenth of the value of the 1 in 81.794. What value is represented by the 1 in the other   number?

5.NBT.1

---

5. What is the value of the expression below?

$$8944 \div 43$$

5.NBT.6

---

6. Abby knocked down 3,113 pins in 11 games. How many pins did she get per game?

5.NBT.6

 **DAY 3**

If there is a zero in the dividend, don't forget to hold that place in the quotient if necessary.

 TIP of the DAY

---

1. What is 6,050 divided (A) by 25? (B) by 10?

5.NBT.6

---

2. What is the value of the expression below?

$$11.91 + 71.2$$

5.NBT.7

---

3. What is the value of the expression below?

$$48.56 \times 7.9$$

5.NBT.7

---

4. Which term can be put in the blank to make the statement true?

$$860,000 = 86 \underline{\hspace{3cm}}$$

5.NBT.1

---

5. What is the value of the expression below?

$$487.49 \div 2.9$$

5.NBT.7

---

6. What is the value of the expression below?

$$2390 - 483.57$$

5.NBT.7

When working on word problems, first identify if you need to add, subtract, multiply or divide.

DAY 4

---

1. Explain how you know that 980.6 + 213.54 does not equal 767.06.

5.NBT.7

---

2. Alex bought some Halloween candy. One large bag cost $19.07, a medium bag cost $11.94 and the third bag cost $8. How much did Alex spend on candy?

5.NBT.7

---

3. Ann had 27.5 gallons of gas in her car. She used up 15.7 gallons. How many gallons remain in her car?

5.NBT.7

---

4. What is the value of the expression below?

$$5107.2 \div 32$$

5.NBT.7

---

5. There was a biking relay across the state. There were 27 bikers and they each traveled 59 kilometers. How far was the race?

5.NBT.5

---

6. Write 9645.8 in (A) words and (B) expanded form.

5.NBT.3

 # DAY 5: ASSESSMENT

1. Use 129.94 and 8.9 to find (A) their sum and (B) their quotient.

5.NBT.7

2. Adam had 3,510.4 pounds of sand that he had to spread over 16 driveways. How much sand should each driveway get?

5.NBT.7

3. Use 138.4 and 8.2 to find (A) their difference and (B) their product.

5.NBT.7

4. If the gym teacher evenly split 1,311 dodge balls among 23 schools, how many dodge balls did each school receive?

5.NBT.6

5. Asher had 60 yards of edging to outline his garden. If he needed 86.3 yards, how many more yards of edging did Asher need?

5.NBT.7

6. Amber worked 46.8 hours, Amanda worked 15 hours and Arnie worked 37.5 hours. What was the combined number of hours they worked?

5.NBT.7

 # DAY 6
CHALLENGE
QUESTION

Bart caught 96.8 inches of fish on Monday, 117.39 on Tuesday. He said he caught 300 inches of fish Monday – Wednesday. If this is true, how many inches of fish did Bart catch on Wednesday?

5.NBT.7

This week you will be able to try taking English phrases and turning them into math. Week 5 also gives practice recognizing how 2 different patterns compare to each other.

You can find detailed video explanations to each problem in the book by visiting:
ArgoPrep.com

DAY 1

When working with more than 1 set of grouping symbols, start on the ones inside and "work your way out" to those symbols that are on the outside.

TIP of the DAY

---

1. What is the value of the expression below?

$$[46 - (8 \times 3) + 10] \div 4$$

5.OA.1

---

2. What is the value of the expression below?

$$[3 \times (2 \times 6)] \div 3$$

5.OA.1

---

3. Bristol had 4,270 pounds of compost that she needed to spread among 14 gardens. How many pounds of compost should each garden get?

5.NBT.6

---

4. What is the value of the expression below?

$$10 \times [13 + 5(6 \times 2) - 10]$$

5.OA.1

---

5. Write 6×10^4 (A) in standard form and (B) in words.

5.NBT.3

---

6. Use words to write a phrase that means $3 \times (7 + 5)$.

5.OA.2

TIP of the **DAY** — Find the values inside grouping symbols (parentheses, brackets, braces) before finding products and quotients.

DAY 2

---

1. What is the value of the expression below?

$$13 + [9 × (3 × 2) – 12] × 4$$

5.OA.1

---

2. Use words to write a phrase that means the same as (5 × 8) + 3.

5.OA.2

---

3. What is the value of the expression below?

$$87 – [6 + (4 × 7) + 1] ÷ 5$$

5.OA.1

---

4. Use words to write a phrase that is the same as (8 × 7) - 11

5.OA.2

---

5. Use 8,751 and 542.39 to find the (A) sum and (B) difference of the 2 numbers.

5.NBT.7

---

6. What is 4213.715 rounded to the nearest (A) tenth? (B) thousandth?

5.NBT.4

DAY 3

Be sure to follow the grouping symbols such as parentheses, braces and brackets. They will help you know which operation to do and in what order.

TIP of the DAY

---

1. What is the value of 8 + (12 − 2 × 2) + 13?

5.OA.1

---

2. Use words to write a phrase that is the same as (15 ÷ 3) + 12

5.OA.2

---

3. Use 2,700 and 2.7 to find (A) the product and (B) the quotient of the 2 numbers.

5.NBT.7

---

4. What is the product of 1376 and 41?

5.NBT.5

---

5. What is the value of the expression below?

$$106 - (45 \div 5) + 4$$

5.OA.1

---

6. Use words to write a phrase that is the same as (19 + 11) ÷ 10

5.OA.2

TIP of the **DAY**

Parentheses are important as their placement can produce different results.
Example: (4 + 9) × 5 ≠ 4 + 9 × 5

DAY 4

---

1. Write a statement comparing the values of the two expressions below.

Expression A: (25 − 8)
Expression B: (25 − 8) + 7

5.OA.2

---

2. Write a mathematical expression that is equivalent to the phrase below.

Add 7 to 35, and then multiply by 4.

5.OA.2

---

3. Write $(7 \times 1000) + (5 \times 100) + (4 \times 10) + (3 \times 1) + \left(6 \times \dfrac{1}{100}\right)$ in (A) words and (B) standard form.

5.NBT.3

---

4. Write a statement that is true about the values of the two expressions below.

Expression A: (5 × 12) × 10
Expression B: (5 × 12)

5.OA.2

---

5. Write a mathematical expression that is equivalent to the phrase below.

Triple the sum of 6 and 11.

5.OA.2

---

6. The digit 5 in 40,675 is _____ times the value of the 5 in 71,350.

5.NBT.1

 # DAY 5: ASSESSMENT

1. What is the value of the expression below?

$$248 - [(2 × 6) + 28] ÷ 4$$

5.OA.1

2. What is the value of 7 × (8 + 7)?

5.OA.1

3. Write a mathematical expression that is equivalent to the phrase below.

The sum of 21 and 8 is divided by 9.

5.OA.2

4. Write a statement comparing the values of the two expressions below.

Expression A: (18 × 7)
Expression B: (18 × 7) – 3

5.OA.2

5. What is the (A) product and (B) quotient of 6.08 and 1000?

5.NBT.2

6. Write 471.5 in (A) words and (B) expanded form.

5.NBT.3

 # DAY 6

CHALLENGE QUESTION

Write a number sentence for the phrase "eight more than the product of two and six".

5.OA.2

WEEK 6

ARGOPREP.COM

VIDEO EXPLANATIONS

During Week 6, you will have more opportunities to develop the skills needed to compare number patterns and even to create your own number patterns.

You can find detailed video explanations to each problem in the book by visiting:
ArgoPrep.com

DAY 1

Sometimes when a phrase says "5 less than 9" you may want to write 5 − 9. This is incorrect, it would be 9 − 5.

1. Write a mathematical expression that is equivalent to the phrase below.

   Two less than the product of nine and six

   5.OA.2

2. Write a statement that is true comparing the values of the two expressions below.

   Expression A: 4 × (10 + 7)
   Expression B: (10 + 7)

   5.OA.2

3. Write a mathematical expression that is equivalent to the phrase below.

   Five more than the product of fourteen and two.

   5.OA.2

4. Write a mathematical expression that is equivalent to the phrase below.

   Nine more than the quotient of 75 and 5.

   5.OA.2

5. Write a statement that is true about the values of the two expressions below.

   Expression A: (9 × 31) − 8
   Expression B: (9 × 31)

   5.OA.2

6. Write a number that has a 3 with a value that is $\frac{1}{10}$ the value of the 3 in 453,261.

   5.NBT.1

When you are studying, remember to take a break. A break allows your brain to rest. To break, you can take a walk, read a book, or just go outside for a bit.

DAY 2

---

1. Use words to write a phrase that best describes the expression below.

$$4 \times (19 - 7)$$

5.OA.2

---

2. What is the value of $(2 + 5) \times 4 \div 2$?

5.OA.1

---

3. Write a true statement comparing the values of the two expressions below.

Expression A: $(12 + 57) \times 8$
Expression B: $(12 + 57)$

5.OA.2

---

4. Write a mathematical expression to describe the phrase below.

Double the difference between 12 and 5.

5.OA.2

---

5. The steaks cost $25.75, drinks $14 and they left a $8.41 tip. (A) How much did just the food and drinks cost? (B) How much did the entire meal cost?

5.NBT.7

---

6. Write 9071.05 in (A) words and (B) expanded form.

5.NBT.3

39

When given 2 patterns, try to find how they relate to each other. Is one half of the other? Is one 3 more than the other?

TIP of the DAY

---

1. Write a phrase to describe the expression below.

$$(10 × 6) - 12$$

5.OA.2

---

2. There are two number patterns below.

Pattern A: 2, 4, 6, 8, ...
Pattern B: 1, 3, 5, 7, ---

Write a statement to describe the patterns.

5.OA.3

The table below shows the cost of several gallons of milk. Use the table to answer questions 3 – 4.

Gallons of Milk	Cost (dollars)
2	6
4	12
6	18

---

3. What is the cost for 3 gallons of milk?

5.OA.3

---

4. What would you expect the cost of 10 gallons of milk to be?

5.OA.3

---

5. Round 17,325.098 to the nearest (A) hundred and (B) hundredth.

5.NBT.4

When looking at graphs and data, be sure to check any labels and units to fully understand what information is being shown.

---

1. There are two number patterns below.

   Pattern A: 3, 6, 9, 12, ...
   Pattern B: 1, 2, 3, 4, ...

   Write a statement about the patterns.

   5.OA.3

The graph below shows the number of miles Brent ran per day. Days are on the horizontal x-axis and the number of miles run is on the vertical y-axis. Use the graph below to answer questions 2 – 4.

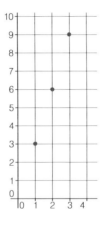

---

2. On what day did Brent run 9 miles?

   5.OA.3

---

3. How many miles would Brent run on Day 5?

   5.OA.3

---

4. How many miles did Brent run on Days 1 - 3 combined?

   5.OA.3

---

5. The number 175.49 is given. In a different number, the 5 represents a value which is one-tenth of the value of the 5 in 175.49. What value is represented by the 5 in the other number?

   5.NBT.1

1. Write a mathematical expression described by the phrase below.

Sixteen more than the product of nine and two.

5.OA.2

The chart below shows the cost for t-shirts. Use the chart to answer questions 2 – 3.

T-shirts	Cost (dollars)
1	4
2	8
3	12

2. What would you expect to be the cost for (A) 5 t-shirts? (B) 8 t-shirts?

5.OA.3

3. What is the relationship between t-shirts and cost?

5.OA.3

4. There are two number patterns below.

Pattern A: 2, 4, 6, 8, ...
Pattern B: 4, 8, 12, 16, ...

Write a statement that describes the patterns.

5.OA.3

5. Which equation is shown in the model below?

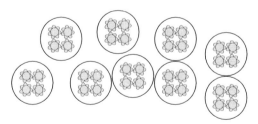

5.NBT.6

 **DAY 6**
CHALLENGE
QUESTION

Write 2 expressions that mean "four times the sum of five and twelve".

5.OA.2

42

Now that you've mastered decimal calculations, Week 7 will give you practice working with fractions. Do well!

You can find detailed video explanations to each problem in the book by visiting: ArgoPrep.com

To add or subtract fractions, they must have the same denominator.

1. $7\dfrac{4}{5} + 8\dfrac{1}{4} = ?$

5.NF.1

2. What is the difference between $39\dfrac{8}{9}$ and $7\dfrac{1}{3}$?

5.NF.1

3. Find: $\dfrac{3}{4} + \dfrac{1}{7}$

5.NF.1

4. What is $56 - 37\dfrac{1}{6}$?

5.NF.1

5. Which expression is the same as 3×10^5?

5.NBT.2

6. What is the value of $[3 \times (4 + 6)] \div 2$?

5.OA.1

TIP of the **DAY**

If a fraction being subtracted is larger than the first fraction, remember to subtract 1 from the whole number to add to the first fraction so you have "enough" to subtract the fraction.

DAY 2

---

1. $93\frac{1}{5} - 32\frac{2}{3} = ?$

5.NF.1

---

2. What is the sum of 45 and $62\frac{3}{8}$?

5.NF.1

---

3. Find: $\frac{7}{8} - \frac{3}{4}$

5.NF.1

---

4. What is $4\frac{3}{5} + 3\frac{3}{6}$?

5.NF.1

---

5. What is the value of the expression below?

$$2 \times [6 + (100 - 54)] + 9$$

5.OA.1

---

6. What is 25.0198 rounded to the nearest (A) tenth (B) thousandth?

5.NBT.4

DAY 3

If the sum of fractions > 1, change the improper fraction to a mixed number.

TIP of the **DAY**

---

1. What is the difference between $32\frac{1}{7}$ and 17?

5.NF.1

---

2. What is $42\frac{3}{8} + 7\frac{1}{4}$?

5.NF.1

---

3. $11\frac{4}{5} + 35\frac{3}{8} = ?$

5.NF.1

---

4. What is the product of 2,980 and 47?

5.NBT.5

---

5. Find: $\frac{3}{8} + \frac{5}{6}$

5.NF.1

---

6. What is $300 - 178\frac{5}{9}$?

5.NF.1

TIP of the **DAY**

Anytime you take an assessment, you should always check your answers to see if they are reasonable.

DAY 4

---

1. What is $81 \frac{9}{11} + 19 \frac{1}{2}$?

5.NF.1

---

2. Find: $76 \frac{1}{5} - 9 \frac{2}{3}$

5.NF.1

---

3. What is the difference between $67 \frac{1}{2}$ and $36 \frac{2}{3}$?

5.NF.1

---

4. Find: $\frac{2}{3} + \frac{1}{6} + \frac{3}{4}$

5.NF.1

---

5. The digit 6 in 47,649 is _____ times the value of the 6 in 86,431.

5.NBT.1

---

6. Write 2,694.503 (A) in expanded form and (B) in words.

5.NBT.3

DAY 5: ASSESSMENT

---

1. What is $49\frac{1}{2} - 18\frac{3}{5}$?

5.NF.1

---

2. Find: $295\frac{1}{2} + 614\frac{1}{8}$

5.NF.1

---

3. What is the (A) sum and (B) difference of 100 and $41\frac{3}{7}$?

5.NF.1

---

4. Find the (A) sum and (B) product of 17.89 and 3.615.

5.NBT.7

---

5. What is the (A) product and (B) quotient of 312,950 and 1000?

5.NBT.2

DAY 6
CHALLENGE QUESTION

Find the value of: $8\frac{3}{8} + 21\frac{1}{2} - 15\frac{3}{4}$

5.NF.1

ARGOPREP.COM

VIDEO EXPLANATIONS

You will get additional practice with fractions during Week 8. Real-world problems are also given to help you understand how fractions are used every day.

You can find detailed video explanations to each problem in the book by visiting:
ArgoPrep.com

 **DAY 1**

It is helpful to know there are only 4 operations that may be used in word problems – addition, subtraction, multiplication or division.

1. If $\frac{3}{4}$ of the trip it was raining, (A) write an equation to find D, the fraction of the trip that it was NOT raining. (B) What fraction of the trip was dry?

5.NF.2

There were 4-person teams that would run 1 mile in total. Below you can see how much of a mile 3 of the teammates ran. Use the table below to answer questions 2 – 4.

Arial	$\frac{1}{4}$
Boris	$\frac{1}{3}$
Bruce	$\frac{1}{8}$

2. What fraction of a mile did the 4th team member need to run?

5.NF.2

3. How much of a mile did Arial and Boris run together?

5.NF.2

4. How much less did Bruce run than Boris?

5.NF.2

5. What is the product of 6,172 and 43?

5.NBT.5

When talking about a group of people, remember that the group is one whole. For example, if 1/3 of the people were wearing red, then 2/3 of the people must NOT have been wearing red.

DAY 2

Ms. Stower's class took a survey of 5th graders to see what their favorite color was. The results are shown below. Use the results to answer questions 1 – 3.

Blue	$\frac{1}{3}$
Red	$\frac{1}{4}$
Purple	$\frac{1}{8}$
Green	$\frac{1}{12}$

1. What fraction of 5th graders liked either blue or red?

5.NF.1

2. What is the difference between those who liked purple and those who liked green?

5.NF.1

3. What fraction of the 5th graders surveyed liked something OTHER than the 4 colors listed?

5.NF.2

4. Bowen thought that $\frac{2}{3} + \frac{1}{4}$ equaled $\frac{3}{7}$. How do you know this answer is incorrect?

5.NF.2

5. Write an expression that shows 69.23 in (A) expanded form and (B) words.

5.NBT.3

DAY 3   You are learning a lot about fractions and how to add and subtract them – good effort – keep it up!

Crystal and Cormick planted a very large garden over the summer. The amount of each vegetable they planted is shown below (in acres). Use this information to answer questions 1 – 4.

Type of Vegetable	Crystal	Cormick
Soybeans	$3\frac{1}{8}$	$2\frac{1}{8}$
Corn	$4\frac{2}{3}$	$5\frac{7}{9}$
Tomatoes	$5\frac{1}{4}$	$4\frac{3}{5}$

1. How many acres did Crystal use for her vegetables?

5.NF.2

2. How many acres of tomatoes were planted?

5.NF.2

3. How many acres of corn were planted?

5.NF.2

4. How many more acres of tomatoes were planted than soybeans?

5.NF.2

5. What is the (A) quotient and (B) difference between 493.5 and 4.7?

5.NBT.7

Don't forget you will need to find a common denominator when adding fractions or mixed numbers.

DAY 4

The fruit basket held 4 different kinds of fruit. Three of the fruits and their amounts are shown below. Use the table to answer questions 1 – 3.

Strawberries	$\frac{1}{9}$
Grapes	$\frac{2}{3}$
Apples	$\frac{1}{6}$

1. What fraction of the fruit basket is not included in the table above?

5.NF.2

2. What fraction of the fruit was either strawberries or apples?

5.NF.2

3. What fraction of the fruit basket was either apples or grapes?

5.NF.2

4. (A) Round 16.397 to the tenths and the hundredths. (B) Use those 2 rounded numbers to write a number sentence that compares the 2 rounded values.

5.NBT.4

5. The number 5178.9 is given. In a different number, the 9 represents a value which is ten times of the value of the 9 in 5178.9. What value is represented by the 9 in the other number?

5.NBT.1

DAY 5: ASSESSMENT

Calista, Chloe, Denver and Dixon ate an entire coconut cream pie. Three of the people's amounts are shown below. Use the information to answer questions 1 – 3.

Calista	$\frac{1}{10}$
Chloe	$\frac{1}{3}$
Denver	$\frac{1}{5}$

1. How much did Chloe and Denver eat together?

5.NF.2

2. How much more did Chloe eat than Calista?

5.NF.2

3. How much pie did Dixon eat?

5.NF.2

4. While Bryce was training for the Olympics, he ran 17 miles per day. How many miles would he run in a month that has 31 days?

5.NBT.5

5. Draw a model that shows $\frac{1}{3}$ being added to $\frac{1}{4}$. What is the result?

5.NF.2

DAY 6
CHALLENGE QUESTION

Why is it impossible for the equation $\frac{1}{3} + \frac{1}{4} = \frac{1}{5}$ to be true?

5.NF.2

Week 9 allows you practice to set up your own division problems involving fractions using real-world problems. Good luck!

You can find detailed video explanations to each problem in the book by visiting:
ArgoPrep.com

 **DAY 1**

A fraction is really another way to write division. $\frac{12}{7}$ means that there are 12 "things" being split among 7 people or other items like boxes or days.

 **TIP** of the **DAY**

---

1. There are 16 people who will be sharing 3 gallons of tea. (A) Write an equation that can be used to find the amount of tea, *T*, each person will receive. (B) How much tea will each person receive?

5.NF.3

---

2. There will be 10 pounds of flour put evenly into 7 sacks. How many pounds of flour will be in each sack? (A) Write an equation that can be used to find the amount of flour, *F*, each sack will contain. (B) How much flour will be in each sack?

5.NF.3

---

3. If Carmen, Dionne, Alisa and Dave each ate a $\frac{3}{4}$ pound burger, how many pounds of hamburger did the restaurant start with?

5.NF.3

---

4. What is the value of the expression below?

$$16 + 64 \div (22 - 6) \times 2$$

5.OA.1

---

5. Drew, Dexter and Ellen are sharing 6 ham and 4 roast beef sandwiches. (A) Write an equation that can be used to find how many sandwiches, *S*, each person will receive. (B) How many sandwiches will each person will receive?

5.NF.3

---

6. The gymnasts cut a 36-foot ribbon into 5 equal pieces for their routine. How long was each piece of ribbon?

5.NF.3

TIP of the DAY In fractions, the denominator (bottom number) indicates the number being divided by, or the number in one whole.

DAY 2

---

1. A box of crackers is 850 grams and one serving is 30 grams. (A) Write an equation to find C, the number of servings. (B) How many servings are in the box of crackers?

5.NF.3

---

2. There were 5000 milliliters of fruit punch to be poured into 36 pitchers. How many milliliters of punch would each pitcher have?

5.NF.3

---

3. There are 426 pounds of peaches to be placed into crates. If there are 18 crates, how many pounds will be in each crate?

5.NF.3

---

4. There are 30 people who will be sharing 84 liters of coffee. (A) Write an equation that can be used to find how much coffee, C, each person received. (B) How many liters of coffee will each person receive?

5.NF.3

---

5. Twenty-four tiny homes are being built from 15 pallets of wood. How many pallets will each home use?

5.NF.3

---

6. What is 713.9244 rounded to the nearest thousandth?

5.NBT.4

DAY 3

Remember a fraction has 2 numbers and represents division – the numerator is being divided by the denominator so $\frac{9}{4}$ means 9 divided by 4.

A number of plants are in a garden and they are shown below. Use the information given to answer questions 1 – 3.

Carrots	22
Lettuce	18
Potatoes	30

1. If there are 5 farmers and all the plants are divided evenly, how many plants will each farmer get?

5.NF.3

2. If only the lettuce plants are divided among the 5 farmers, how many lettuce plants will each farmer get?

5.NF.3

3. If the carrots and potatoes are divided among the 5 farmers, how many plants will each farmer get?

5.NF.3

4. If Dinah, Edward and Felix each ate $\frac{5}{3}$ cups of granola, how many cups of granola were there to start?

5.NF.3

5. Fred and Esme each ate $\frac{1}{4}$ of the pizza and Fern ate $\frac{1}{3}$. How much of the pizza is left?

5.NF.2

As you answer word problems, try to understand if division is involved and if so, look to find which number is being divided by which number.

DAY 4

1. The trip was 698 miles. If they took 7 days to travel, how many miles did they travel per day?

5.NF.3

2. There are 24 people who will be sharing 15 kg of rice. (A) Write an equation that can be used to find the amount of rice, R, each person will receive. (B) How much rice will each person receive?

5.NF.3

The chart below shows 3 different bike trails. Use the information below to answer questions 3 – 4.

Kings Mountain Trail	18 miles
Boston Bridge Trail	26 miles
Beverly Springs Trail	15 miles

3. If the bikers covered all 3 races in 4 days, how many miles would they need to bike each day?

5.NF.3

4. How many miles would they travel per day if they completed the Kings Mountain and Beverly Springs trails in 3 days?

5.NF.3

5. The digit 4 in 14,920 is _____ times the value of the 4 in 7,435.

5.NBT.1

 # DAY 5: ASSESSMENT

1. A runner ran 37 miles in 6 hours. About how many miles did she run per hour?

5.NF.3

2. There are 21 people who will each be walking a section of a trail that is 133 miles long. If each person walks the same distance, how many miles will each one walk?

5.NF.3

3. There are 12 cups of raisins that can be split among 5 people. (A) Write an equation that can be used to find how many cups of raisins, *R*, each person would get. (B) If everyone gets the same amount, how many cups of raisins will each person get?

5.NF.3

4. Write a statement about the values of the two expressions below.

Expression A: (398 × 17) − 8
Expression B: (398 × 17)

5.OA.2

5. The counselor cut a 165-foot roll of leather into 75 equal pieces, one for each camper. How much leather did each camper receive?

5.NF.3

6. There will be 51 pounds of beans put evenly into 17 bags. (A) Write an equation that can be used to find how many pounds of beans, *B*, will be in each bag. (B) How many pounds of beans will be in each bag?

5.NF.3

 # DAY 6
CHALLENGE QUESTION

There are 13 people on a team. If each team member runs $\frac{7}{13}$ of a kilometer, how many kilometers in total was the race?

5.NF.3

Week 10 lets you try your hand at multiplying fractions by whole numbers and fractions by other fractions. Areas of different rectangles are calculated as well.

You can find detailed video explanations to each problem in the book by visiting: ArgoPrep.com

DAY 1

Don't forget that a whole number can be written as a fraction. The number 8 can be written as $\frac{8}{1}$.

TIP of the DAY

1. The shaded part of the square below has a width of $\frac{1}{2}$ inch and a length of $\frac{6}{7}$ inch.

— 1 in —

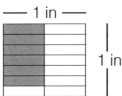

1 in

(A) Write an equation that could be used to find the area, *A*, of the shaded portion. (B) What is the area, in square inches, of the shaded part of the square?

5.NF.4

2. Write the equation that is being modeled below.

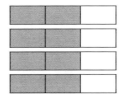

5.NF.4

3. Write a mathematical expression that is equivalent to the phrase below.

Eight less than the product of nine and twelve .

5.OA.2

4. The floor of the stage measures $\frac{3}{5}$ meters long and $\frac{6}{7}$ meters wide. What is the area of the stage floor?

5.NF.4

5. (A) Draw a model that shows $\frac{2}{3} \times \frac{6}{7}$ (B) What is the product of $\frac{2}{3} \times \frac{6}{7}$?

5.NF.4

6. Write an equation that could be shown by the model below.

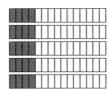

5.NF.4

 **of the DAY**

When multiplying fractions, multiply the numerators together and then multiply the denominators together. If possible, you should reduce/simplify.

DAY 2

---

1. Write the equation that is modeled below.

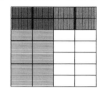

5.NF.4

---

2. (A) Write an equation that can be used to find A, the area of the rectangle below. (B) What is its area?

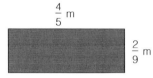

$\frac{4}{5}$ m

$\frac{2}{9}$ m

5.NF.4

---

3. What is the product of $\frac{2}{5} \times \frac{3}{8}$?

5.NF.4

---

4. The shaded part of the square below has a width of $\frac{3}{4}$ yard and a length of $\frac{3}{5}$ yard.

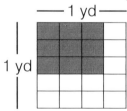

— 1 yd —

1 yd

(A) Write an equation that could be used to find A, the area of the shaded part. (B) What is the area, in square yards, of the shaded part of the square?

5.NF.4

---

5. The doormat measures $\frac{1}{6}$ meter wide and $\frac{2}{3}$ meter long. What is the area of the mat?

5.NF.4

---

6. Write an equation for the model below.

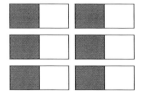

5.NF.4

DAY 3

When a proper fraction is multiplied by a whole number other than 1, the product is a number greater than the fraction but less than the whole number.

---

1. The shaded part of the square below has a length of $\frac{4}{7}$ foot and a width of $\frac{5}{6}$ foot.

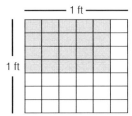

(A) What equation can be used to find *A*, the area of the shaded part? (B) What is the area, in square feet, of the shaded part of the square?   5.NF.4

---

2. Write the equation that is being modeled below.

5.NF.4

---

3. There are 48 ounces of lemonade that 5 people will share. The number of ounces of lemonade each person will get is between what 2 numbers?   5.NF.3

The table below shows the costs of some pairs of socks. Use the table to answer questions 4 – 5.

Socks	Cost
2	10
4	20
6	30

4. What is the cost for 3 pairs of socks?   5.OA.3

---

5. What would you expect the cost of 9 pairs of socks to be?   5.OA.3

---

6. What is the area of the rectangle shown below?

$\frac{5}{7}$ in

$\frac{7}{10}$ in

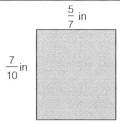

5.NF.4

TIP of the **DAY**

A factor is a number that is being multiplied. In 4 × 7 = 28, 4 and 7 are the factors and 28 is the product.

DAY 4

---

1. The shaded part of the square below has a length of $\frac{5}{6}$ meter and a width of $\frac{2}{5}$ meter.

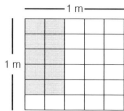

(A) Write the equation that could be used to find A, the area of the shaded part. (B) What is the area, in square meters, of the shaded part of the square?

5.NF.4

---

2. Nine wrenches have a mass of 943 grams. The number of grams per wrench is between what 2 numbers?

5.NF.3

---

3. What is the area of the rectangle shown below?

$\frac{3}{5}$ yd $\frac{3}{4}$ yd

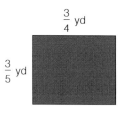

5.NF.4

---

4. Write the equation that is being modeled below.

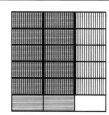

5.NF.4

---

5. What is the product of $\frac{4}{7} \times \frac{2}{3}$?

5.NF.4

---

6. The flag measures $\frac{4}{5}$ yards long and $\frac{2}{3}$ yards wide. How much material would be needed to make the flag?

5.NF.4

1. (A) Draw a diagram to represent $\frac{4}{5} \times \frac{1}{8}$. (B) What is the product of $\frac{4}{5} \times \frac{1}{8}$?

5.NF.4

2. A small quilt measures $\frac{4}{5}$ yards long and $\frac{3}{7}$ yards wide. What is the area of the quilt?

5.NF.4

3. There are 70 grams of salt that will be used in 8 recipes. The number of grams of salt each recipe will get is between what 2 numbers?

5.NF.3

4. What is the area of the rectangle shown below?

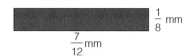

$\frac{1}{8}$ mm

$\frac{7}{12}$ mm

5.NF.4

5. There are two number patterns below.

Pattern A: 1, 3, 5, 7, ...
Pattern B: 3, 9, 15, 21, ---

Write a statement that describes the relationship between the 2 patterns.

5.OA.3

6. What equation could be used to describe the model below?

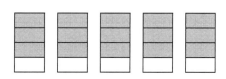

5.NF.4

 **DAY 6** CHALLENGE QUESTION A sidewalk measures $\frac{5}{4}$ meter by $\frac{1}{3}$ meter. What is the area of the sidewalk?

5.NF.4

This week (Week 11) you will have a chance to show your understanding of what a product should be, based only on the factors, without even multiplying them out!

You can find detailed video explanations to each problem in the book by visiting:
ArgoPrep.com

If a number is multiplied by a fraction that is < 1, the product will be less than that number.

TIP of the DAY

---

1. What can you predict about the product of $\dfrac{6}{5} \times \dfrac{7}{3}$? How do you know?

5.NF.5

---

2. Gwendolyn is saving to buy a computer. Each pay period she is able to save $\dfrac{2}{9}$ of the cost of the computer. How many pay periods will it take before she can buy a computer?

5.NF.5

---

3. How do you know that $\dfrac{1}{6} \times 8$ will be less than 8? Use a model to show your answer.

5.NF.5

---

4. What could you tell a classmate about the product of $\dfrac{8}{8} \times 12$ and how do you know what you say is true?

5.NF.5

---

5. Grant was reading a book for school. If he could read $\dfrac{2}{13}$ of the book each day, how many days would it take before he had completely read the book?

5.NF.5

---

6. Conrad multiplied the number 9 by another number and the product was less than 9. Write a fraction that Conrad could have used to multiply the 9 by.

5.NF.5

TIP of the **DAY** If a whole number is multiplied by a fraction that is greater than 1, the product will be greater than the whole number.

DAY 2

---

1. How do you know that $\frac{7}{4} \times 5$ will be more than 5? Show your work using a model.

5.NF.5

---

2. Garrison is saving his money to buy a bike. Each month he is able to set aside $\frac{3}{12}$ of the money needed. (A) How many months before Garrison has enough for the bike? (B) Will he have *exactly* enough or will there be some extra?

5.NF.5

---

3. What could you tell a classmate about the product of $\frac{4}{4} \times 9$ and how do you know what you say is true?

5.NF.5

---

4. Ian is saving to buy a car. Every month he is able to save $\frac{3}{8}$ of the cost of the car. (A) How many months will it take before he can buy a car? (B) Will he have exactly enough for the car or will he have extra?

5.NF.5

---

5. What could you tell a classmate about the product of $18 \times \frac{7}{8}$?

5.NF.5

---

6. Seventeen quarts of water were held in 3 containers. How many quarts were in each container?

5.NF.3

DAY 3

If a number is multiplied by a fraction that is equal to 1, then the product will be equal to the original number.

TIP of the DAY

---

1. Bartoli is picking olives. He is able to pick $\frac{1}{8}$ pound per minute. How many minutes will it take him to pick 1 pound?

5.NF.5

---

2. Kelvin multiplies the number 12 by another number and the product is larger than 12. Write a fraction that Kelvin could have used to multiply the 12 by.

5.NF.5

---

3. What could you tell a classmate about the product of $11 \times \frac{4}{9}$?

5.NF.5

---

4. How do you know that $\frac{4}{5} \times 10$ will be less than 10? Show your work using a model.

5.NF.5

---

5. What is the product of 319 and 1,428?

5.NBT.5

---

6. Gracie is planting a garden. If she is able to plant $\frac{1}{5}$ of the garden in a week, how long will it take her to plant the entire garden?

5.NF.5

TIP of the **DAY**

When multiplying a whole number by a fraction, find out if the fraction is < 1, > 1 or = 1. This step will let you know if the answer should be more than, less than or equal to the whole number.

DAY 4

1. If Harold mows $\frac{3}{7}$ of an acre per hour, how many hours will it take for him to mow 3 acres?

5.NF.5

2. How do you know that $\frac{5}{5} \times 4$ will be equal to 4? Show your work using a model.

5.NF.5

3. What could you tell a classmate about the product of $\frac{1}{7} \times 9$?

5.NF.5

4. Jared was placing 21 pencils in a bag. If he was bagging 8,295 pencils, how many bags would he need to bag all of the pencils?

5.NBT.6

5. Jess multiplies the number 6 by another number and the product is 6. Write a fraction that Jess could have used to multiply the 6 by.

5.NF.5

6. How do you know that $3 \times \frac{3}{2}$ will be more than 3? Show your work using a model.

5.NF.5

DAY 5: ASSESSMENT

---

1. What could you tell a classmate about the product of $\frac{3}{3} \times 7$ and how do you know what you say is true?

   5.NF.5

---

2. Elsa multiplies the number 11 by another number and the product is < 11. Write a fraction that Elsa could have used to multiply by 11.

   5.NF.5

---

3. What could you tell a classmate about the product of $\frac{3}{5} \times \frac{2}{9}$? Explain why.

   5.NF.5

---

4. Jimmy drove $\frac{2}{9}$ of the trip in 1 hour. What is the minimum number of hours it would take Jimmy to complete the trip?

   5.NF.5

---

5. How do you know that $15 \times \frac{9}{9}$ will be equal to 15? Use a model to show your work.

   5.NF.5

---

6. Jaleesa practiced the tuba $\frac{2}{5}$ of an hour for 3 days. (A) Draw a model that could show the amount of time Jaleesa practiced the tuba. (B) How long did Jalessa practice over the 3 days?

   5.NF.4

DAY 6

CHALLENGE QUESTION

Write a statement that says what you would expect the product to be for $\frac{3}{5} \times 4$.

5.NF.5

Often students really struggle understanding fractions so Week 12 will give you lots of extra practice with real-world problems that involve fractions.

You can find detailed video explanations to each problem in the book by visiting: ArgoPrep.com

DAY 1

When multiplying a mixed number, change it to an improper fraction first.

TIP of the DAY

1. Jill jogged for $3\frac{1}{5}$ hours last week. Jake ran $\frac{1}{2}$ as long. (A) Write an equation that could be used to find J, the number of hours Jake ran. (B) How many hours did Jake run?

5.NF.6

Below is a chart showing how many hours some students spent playing outside. Use the information to answer questions 2 – 4.

Kirstie	$6\frac{2}{5}$
Jayson	$5\frac{7}{8}$
Juan	$2\frac{1}{4}$

2. If Leah played half as long as Kirstie, how long did Leah play?

5.NF.6

3. If Lydia played twice as long as Jayson, how long did Lydia play?

5.NF.6

4. If Jackie played $\frac{2}{3}$ as long as Juan, how long did Jackie play?

5.NF.6

5. What could you tell a classmate about the product of $\frac{7}{5} \times \frac{4}{3}$? Explain your answer.

5.NF.5

6. What is the product of $\frac{4}{3} \times \frac{5}{8}$?

5.NF.4

TIP of the **DAY**

After finding the product of fractions or mixed numbers, check your answer to see if the fraction can be simplified.

DAY 2

Below is a chart showing the mass of 3 different sub sandwiches. Mass is in kg. Use the information to answer questions 1 – 3.

Ham/Cheese	$\dfrac{3}{4}$
Turkey	$\dfrac{3}{3}$
Pastrami	$\dfrac{7}{5}$

---

1. If Jamey bought 8 sandwiches that were all the same and the bag was less than 8 pounds, which type of sandwich did Jamey buy?

5.NF.6

---

2. Alexander purchased 5 of the same type of sandwiches and his bag was over 5 pounds. Which sandwich did Alexander purchase?

5.NF.6

---

3. What would be the mass of (A) 12 (B) 19 and (C) 7 turkey sandwiches?

5.NF.6

---

4. Irina cut $3\dfrac{2}{3}$ inches from her hair in July and $2\dfrac{1}{5}$ more inches in August. How many inches did Irina have cut from her hair?

5.NF.1

---

5. Jane ran $12\dfrac{3}{5}$ km. Jude ran $\dfrac{7}{9}$ as far as Jane. (A) Write an equation that could be used to find J, the number of km that Jude ran. (B) How far did Jude run?

5.NF.6

DAY 3

The more practice you get working with fractions, the easier fractions will become.

TIP of the DAY

1. Karly worked on her science project for $10\frac{1}{5}$ hours on Monday. On Tuesday she worked $\frac{2}{3}$ as long. (A) Write an equation that could be used to find K, the number of hours Karly spent on her project on Tuesday. (B) How many hours did Karly spend on her project on Tuesday?

5.NF.6

The number of cookies that Jerica ate is shown below. Use the information to answer questions 2 – 4.

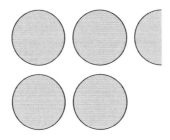

2. If Lulu ate $\frac{1}{2}$ as many cookies as Jerica, how many cookies did Lulu eat?

5.NF.6

3. Hunter ate $1\frac{2}{3}$ times as many cookies as Jerica. How many cookies did Hunter eat?

5.NF.6

4. Ivan ate triple what Jerica ate. How many cookies did Ivan eat?

5.NF.6

5. What is the area of the rectangle below?

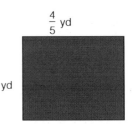

$\frac{4}{5}$ yd

$\frac{2}{3}$ yd

5.NF.4

6. There are 215 dozen donuts that 27 classes will share. The number of dozen that each class will receive is between what 2 numbers?

5.NF.3

TIP of the **DAY** When working on questions, take time to check each answer to see if it makes sense.

DAY 4

Below is a chart showing the distance (in miles) that 3 different students ran in a certain time. Use the information to answer questions 1 – 3.

Jolene	$\dfrac{9}{8}$
Halle	$\dfrac{4}{5}$
Ivy	$\dfrac{7}{7}$

1. If the time was 3 times longer, which student would run more than 3 miles?

5.NF.6

2. If Ivy had 5 times as long to run, how many miles would she run?

5.NF.6

3. What would Halle's distances be if the time were multiplied by (A) 5 and (B) 7 times?

5.NF.6

4. One loaf of bread calls for $1\dfrac{1}{4}$ cups of flour. If Lee makes 5 loaves, how many cups of flour will he need?

5.NF.6

5. Marista uses $14\dfrac{1}{5}$ lemons for her lemonade. Mark uses $\dfrac{3}{4}$ as many lemons for his lemonade. (A) Write an equation that could be used to find M, the number of lemons Mark uses. (B) How many lemons does Mark use?

5.NF.6

6. Write a mathematical expression that means the same as the phrase below.

Thirteen less than the product of 11 and 4.

5.OA.2

DAY 5: ASSESSMENT

1. One serving of fruit punch uses $2\frac{1}{3}$ teaspoons of powder. If a pitcher contains 8 servings, how many teaspoons of powder are needed for a pitcher of punch?

   5.NF.6

2. Kasten grew $2\frac{4}{5}$ inches over the school year. Over the summer he only grew half that amount. (A) Write an equation to find K, the amount Kasten grew over the summer. (B) How many inches did Kasten grow over the summer?

   5.NF.6

3. One rope was $5\frac{3}{5}$ meters long. The second rope was $1\frac{1}{4}$ as long. How many meters long was the second rope?

   5.NF.6

4. What is the quotient when 54,137.82 is divided by (A) 10, (B) 100 and (C) 1,000?

   5.NBT.2

5. Karis practiced the harp for $3\frac{1}{4}$ hours. Nora practiced 3 times that long. (A) Write an equation to find N, the amount of time Nora practiced. (B) How long did Nora practice?

   5.NF.6

6. Place the following numbers in order from smallest to largest.

   73.9   74.16   74.089   74.152

   5.NBT.3

DAY 6

CHALLENGE QUESTION

Luca spent $2\frac{1}{3}$ hours working on his paper. Janna spent 2 times that and Kit spent one-third as much time on her paper. How many hours did Janna and Kit spend on her papers.

5.NF.6

Unit fractions are fractions that have a 1 in the numerator. Week 13 will offer lots of exercises that involve the multiplication or division of unit fractions.

You can find detailed video explanations to each problem in the book by visiting: ArgoPrep.com

DAY 1

When dividing, multiply by the reciprocal of the number being divided by.

TIP of the **DAY**

1. What is the value of the expression: $\frac{1}{9} \div 3$?

5.NF.7

2. There was $\frac{1}{4}$ of a gallon of punch left. Five children shared it. (A) Write an equation to find P, the amount of punch each child would receive. (B) How many gallons would each child have?

5.NF.7

3. What is the value of the expression: $10 \div \frac{1}{5}$?

5.NF.7

4. Liam, Justin and Kenny equally shared $\frac{1}{2}$ of a pie. (A) Write an equation that could be used to find P, the amount of pie each person received. (B) What fraction of the whole pie did they each receive?

5.NF.7

5. Each piece of candy cost $\frac{1}{5}$ of a dollar. Lottie had 5 dollars. (A) Write an equation that could be used to find C, the number of candies Lottie could buy. (B) How many candies could Lottie buy?

5.NF.7

6. What is the (A) sum and (B) difference of $\frac{5}{8}$ and $\frac{1}{3}$?

5.NF.1

TIP of the **DAY** The order of the numbers is important when dividing.

DAY 2

---

1. How many $\frac{1}{4}$ cup servings are in 7 cups of sour cream?

5.NF.7

---

2. What is the value of the expression: $24 \div \frac{1}{4}$?

5.NF.7

---

3. Kurt and his sister split $\frac{1}{3}$ - gallon of ice cream. (A) Write an equation that can be used to find C, the amount of ice cream each person ate. (B) How many gallons of ice cream did each person receive?

5.NF.7

---

4. What is the value of the expression below?

$$20 + 64 \div (3 + 5) \times 2$$

5.OA.1

---

5. What is the value of the expression: $18 \div \frac{1}{4}$?

5.NF.7

---

6. Dee, Ed, Elle and Franco are sharing 7 peanut butter and 9 turkey sandwiches. (A) Write an equation that can be used to find S, the number of sandwiches each person will receive. (B) How many sandwiches will each person will receive?

5.NF.3

DAY 3

A reciprocal is a number where the digits change from numerator to denominator and denominator to numerator. The reciprocal of 7 is $\frac{1}{7}$.

TIP of the DAY

After the BBQ, the caterer had some food leftover. It is shown below. Use the information to answer questions 1 – 4.

Cole slaw	$\frac{1}{3}$ gallon
Ketchup	$\frac{1}{4}$ gallon
Pickles	$\frac{1}{2}$ gallon

1. If 2 people each took home half of the remaining cole slaw, how many gallons would each person take home?

5.NF.7

2. If 3 people split the ketchup, how many gallons would each person receive?

5.NF.7

3. The pickles were divided equally among 4 people. How many gallons did each person receive?

5.NF.7

4. If there was $2\frac{4}{5}$ times as much mustard as ketchup, how many gallons of mustard were there?

5.NF.6

5. What is the (A) product and (B) quotient of 12.738 and 10^3?

5.NBT.2

6. If there were 5,334 cars evenly split among 14 lots, how many cars were on each lot?

5.NBT.6

If a kilogram of almonds were divided into 4 bags that contained the same amount of almonds, each of the 4 bags would weigh $\frac{1}{4}$ of a kilogram.

 **DAY 4**

---

1. What is the value of the expression: $4 \div \frac{1}{5}$?

5.NF.7

---

2. If Leila and Joey walk a combined total of $\frac{1}{3}$ of a mile, and they walk the same distance, how far did each one walk?

5.NF.7

---

3. How many $\frac{1}{2}$-cup servings are in 12 cups of oatmeal?

5.NF.7

---

4. There was $\frac{1}{9}$ of a pound of apples left. Three children shared the apples. (A) Write an equation to find A, the amount of apples each child would receive. (B) How many pounds of apples would each child have?

5.NF.7

---

5. What is the value of the expression below?

$$438.48 \div 3.6$$

5.NBT.7

---

6. Write a number that could round to 8,100 but not 8,090.

5.NBT.4

1. Tim and Louis share $\frac{1}{4}$ of a bag of pretzels. What fraction of the bag does each boy get?

5.NF.7

2. How many $\frac{1}{3}$ gallons are in 7 gallons of gas?

5.NF.7

3. There was $\frac{1}{8}$ of a pound of peanuts left. Four children shared the peanuts. (A) Write an equation to find P, the amount of peanuts each child would receive. (B) How many pounds of peanuts would each child have?

5.NF.7

4. What is the value of the expression: $12 \div \frac{1}{5}$?

5.NF.7

5. Nia multiplies the number 3 by another number and the product is > 3. Write a fraction that Nia could have used to multiply the 3 by.

5.NF.5

6. Olivia has $\frac{1}{2}$ of a bag of peaches to share with her 3 siblings. What fraction of a bag does each of the 4 siblings receive?

5.NF.7

DAY 6
CHALLENGE
QUESTION

There is $\frac{1}{6}$ of a pound of chocolate that 4 people will share. (A) Write an equation that could be used to find C, the amount of chocolate each person would get. (B) What fraction of the pound will each person receive?

5.NF.7

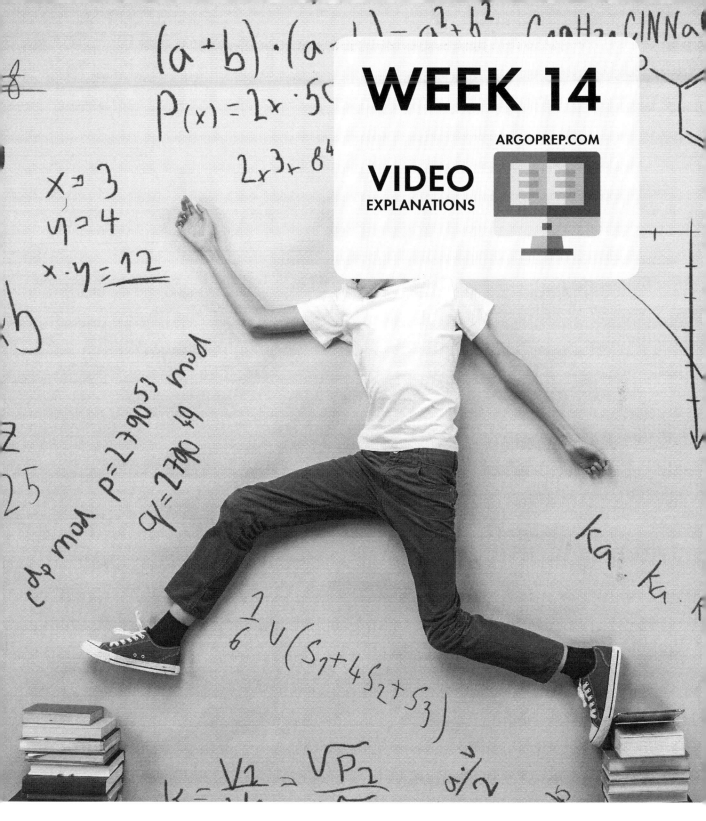

This week (Week 14) will require a lot of converting units. Converting units is just another way to say changing units. You will be asked to change yards to inches or kilograms to grams and other unit conversions.

You can find detailed video explanations to each problem in the book by visiting:
ArgoPrep.com

DAY 1

When working with length or mass, check the units as well as the numbers.

TIP of the DAY

---

1. Lindsay ran 6 km and Paola ran 5,907 m. (A) Who ran farther? (B) How much farther did she run?

5.MD.1

---

2. Oskar is 47 inches tall and his cousin is 5 feet tall. (A) Who is taller and (B) by how many inches?

5.MD.1

---

3. Isabella needs 438 yards of yarn. Each package has 36 feet of yarn. How many packages does Isabella need?

5.MD.1

---

4. The baby weighed 9 pounds and 4 ounces. How many ounces was the baby?

5.MD.1

---

5. Write 72,308.016 in (A) words and (B) in expanded form.

5.NBT.3

---

6. Sherman drove ran 92 km and Mia drove 98,723 m. (A) Who drove farther? (B) How much farther did he or she drive?

5.MD.1

Often when changing units within the Metric System, you may only need to move the decimal point because the Metric System is based on the number 10.

The zookeeper measured 4 animals and recorded their weights below. Use this information to answer questions 1 – 4.

Otter	293 ounces
Penguin	17 pounds, 9 ounces
Chimpanzee	45 pounds
Beaver	435 ounces

1. Which animal weighs (A) the most? (B) the least?

5.MD.1

2. In pounds and ounces, how much more does the Chimpanzee weigh than the otter?

5.MD.1

3. In pounds and ounces, what is the combined weight of the penguin and the beaver?

5.MD.1

4. If all 4 animals were placed on a scale, how much should the scale read in (A) ounces and (B) pounds?

5.MD.1

5. Six people each drank $\frac{5}{6}$ cup of coffee. How many cups of coffee did they share?

5.NF.3

DAY 3

The U.S. Customary Units have many different numbers involved so be sure to know which numbers go with which units. (16 oz = 1 pound, 24 hrs = 1 day, 5,280 ft = 1 mile, etc.)

The amount of time 4 students studied is recorded below. Use this information to answer questions 1 – 3.

Rose	150 minutes
Steven	3 hours
Sharon	2.5 hours
Caroline	143 minutes

1. Which students studied (A) the longest and (B) the shortest amount of time?

5.MD.1

2. Which 2 students studied the same amount of time?

5.MD.1

3. How many minutes longer did Steven study than Sharon?

5.MD.1

4. Gunnar's shoes were 2 pounds and 5 ounces. His boots were 4 pounds and 3 ounces. Answer the 2 questions below in pounds and ounces.

   A. What was the combined weight of Gunnar's footwear?
   B. How much heavier were the boots than the shoes?

5.MD.1

5. Reuben ran 816 meters, then 1,495 meters and finally 6,237 meters. How far did Reuben run altogether in kilometers?

5.MD.1

TIP of the DAY

It is a good idea to review the numbers used when changing to/from units such as hours/day, yards/inches and pounds/ounces.

DAY 4

1. The toy giraffe is 108 centimeters tall. The toy fire engine is 270 millimeters tall. (A) Which toy is taller? (B) How much taller?

    5.MD.1

The chart below shows the weights of 4 different baby animals. Use the chart to answer questions 2 – 4.

Kid (goat)	$3\frac{1}{2}$ pounds
Kitten	35 ounces
Joey (Kangaroo)	43 ounces
Puppy	4 pounds

2. Which animal weighs the most?

    5.MD.1

3. (A) Which weighs more – the kid or the joey? (B) How much more does it weigh?

    5.MD.1

4. How much do all 4 animals weigh combined, in pounds?

    5.MD.1

5. The pencil is 61 millimeters long and the marker is 7 centimeters long. (A) Which writing instrument is longer? (B) How much longer?

    5.MD.1

6. What is the product of 0.0835 and (A) 10, (B) 100, and (C) 1000?

    5.NBT.2

1. The model bell tower was 5 feet in height. The model library was 45 inches tall. (A) Which building was taller? (B) How much taller?

5.MD.1

2. Priscilla lives 5 km from the library. Sabrina lives 5,194 m from the library. (A) Who lives closer to the library? (B) How many km closer does she live?

5.MD.1

3. How many $\frac{1}{3}$ - cup servings are in 14 cups of rice?

5.NF.7

4. One cup of tea requires $\frac{1}{2}$ oz of tea leaves. If a container holds 20 pounds of leaves, how many cups of tea can be made from the container?

5.MD.1

5. The bag of grapefruit weighs 10 pounds and 5 ounces. The bag of limes weighs 139 ounces. (A) Which fruit weighs the most? (B) How much heavier is that fruit?

5.MD.1

6. The table was 29 pounds and 8 ounces. The chair weighed 46 pounds and 3 ounces. Answer the 2 questions below in pounds and ounces.

A. What was the combined weight of the furniture?
B. How much heavier was the chair than the table?

5.MD.1

# DAY 6
CHALLENGE
QUESTION

Each yard of material costs $4.49. Patty is making 2 patterns. One calls for 11 feet and the other calls for 6 feet of material. How much would it cost to buy the material needed?

5.MD.1, 5.NBT.7

Week 15 you will find lots of practice answering questions using sets of data. You will be reading dot plots to find information for real-world scenarios.

You can find detailed video explanations to each problem in the book by visiting:
ArgoPrep.com

DAY 1

When data is arranged in charts or tables, look at ALL the information given, including labels and units.

TIP of the DAY

Below is a data set showing the rainfall on certain days. Use this information to answer questions 1 - 3.

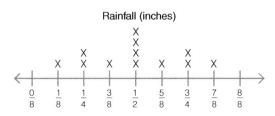

Rainfall (inches)

1. How many days was the rainfall recorded?

5.MD.2

2. What was the total amount of rainfall?

5.MD.2

3. If the total amount remained the same and it rained equally on each of the days, how much rain would there be on 1 day?

5.MD.2

The amount of water that the tennis team drank on Tuesday is shown below. Use this information to answer questions 4 – 6.

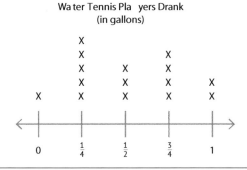

Water Tennis Players Drank (in gallons)

4. How many gallons of water were consumed in total?

5.MD.2

5. How many players drank more than $\frac{1}{2}$ gallon of water?

5.MD.2

6. How many players drank exactly $\frac{1}{4}$ gallon of water?

5.MD.2

TIP of the **DAY**

Dot plots and other graphs show real-world information in a visual format.

DAY 2

There were 10 students who recorded how many inches they grew over the summer. The information is shown below. Use this information to answer question 1 – 3.

Growth (inches)

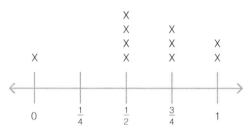

1. How many students grew LESS than $\frac{1}{2}$ inch?

5.MD.2

2. What was the total number of inches that the students grew?

5.MD.2

3. If the students grew the same total amount but each student grew the same as all of the other students, how many inches would each student grow?

5.MD.2

4. How many $\frac{1}{4}$ - cup servings of pudding are in 11 cups of pudding?

5.NF.7

Richard measured some kudzu plants over a month. Their growth is shown below. Use this information to answer questions 5 – 6.

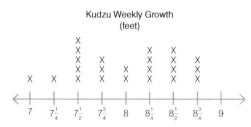

Kudzu Weekly Growth (feet)

5. How many kudzu plants were measured?

5.MD.2

6. How many plants grew MORE than 8 feet that month?

5.MD.2

DAY 3

Before you can add or subtract fractions (or mixed numbers), find the least common denominator (LCD).

Mr. McNair's class collected food for the local food bank. The contributions are shown below. Use the information to answer questions 1 – 3.

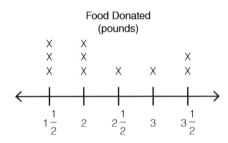

1. How many pounds of food did the class donate?

5.MD.2

2. If the amount collected was the same and everyone gave the same amount, how many pounds would each student give?

5.MD.2

3. How many students brought a donation for the food bank?

5.MD.2

The fifth grade caught frogs and had a jumping contest. The jumps recorded are shown below. Use the information to answer questions 4 – 6.

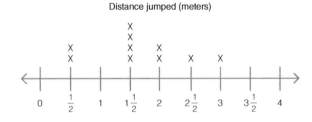

4. What was the distance most frogs jumped?

5.MD.2

5. What was the combined distance jumped by all the frogs?

5.MD.2

6. If the total distance remained the same but each frog jumped the same distance, how many meters would each frog jump?

5.MD.2

TIP of the **DAY**

When working with graphs or charts, make sure you are correctly reading the information.

DAY 4

The lengths of different ropes were measured and the data is shown below. Use the information to answer questions 1 – 3.

Length (feet)

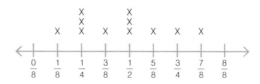

---

1. If all of the ropes were laid end-to-end, how far would they stretch?

5.MD.2

---

2. What is the difference between the longest and the shortest ropes?

5.MD.2

---

3. How many ropes are at least 1 foot long?

5.MD.2

---

4. What is 12.4865 rounded to the nearest hundredth?

5.NBT.4

---

5. Write $(2 \times 1000) + (7 \times 100) + (6 \times 10) + (5 \times 1) + \left(9 \times \dfrac{1}{10}\right)$ in (A) words and (B) standard form.

5.NBT.3

---

6. Write a statement comparing the values of the two expressions below.

Expression A: $(54 \times 72) - 3$
Expression B: 54×72

5.OA.2

Below is some data about the amount of juice Sally drank on certain days. Use the data set to answer questions 1 – 3.

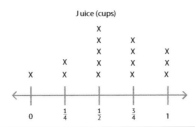

1. How many days was the amount of juice that Sally drank recorded?

   5.MD.2

2. How much juice did Sally drink altogether?

   5.MD.2

3. If the Sally's brother, Charlie, drank $2\frac{1}{3}$ times the amount of juice as Sally, how many cups of juice would Charlie drink?

   5.NF.6

4. What is the area of the rectangle below?

   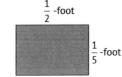

   $\frac{1}{2}$ -foot

   $\frac{1}{5}$ -foot

   5.NF.4

5. If Leo builds $\frac{3}{8}$ of the tree fort in an hour, how many hours would it take him to build the entire fort?

   5.NF.5

6. The number 758.206 is given. In a different number, the 2 represents a value which is ten times of the value of the 2 in 758.206. What value is represented by the 2 in the other number?

   5NBT.1

DAY 6
CHALLENGE QUESTION

Last week Rafael ran 3,200 m on Friday, 3 km on Saturday and 900 m on Sunday. How far did Rafael run altogether?

5.MD.1

Some people naturally do better when they can see three-dimensional shapes. Week 16's lessons have lots of practice finding the volume of three-dimensional figures.

You can find detailed video explanations to each problem in the book by visiting:
ArgoPrep.com

 **DAY 1**

Volume can be found by counting the number of unit cubes that can fit into a particular space.

 **TIP** of the **DAY**

---

1. Stephanie filled a box with unit cubes so that there was no space unfilled. The box had a volume of 480 cubic units. How many unit cubes were in the box?

   5.MD.3

---

2. How many unit cubes are in the box shown below?

   5.MD.3

There were 4 different boxes that Tina filled with unit cubes. The number of cubes used for the width, length and the number of layers are shown. Use this information to answer questions 3 – 5.

Box	Width	Length	Layers
A	3	12	4
B	8	9	2
C	10	5	6
D	4	7	5

---

3. Which box had the largest number of unit cubes?

   5.MD.3

---

4. Which two boxes have the same number of unit cubes?

   5.MD.3

---

5. How many unit cubes were in Box D?

   5.MD.3

---

6. What is the value of 12 + 3 × (7 + 1)?

   5.OA.1

The number of unit cubes that fit into a space is the same number of cubic units that make up the volume of that same space.

DAY 2

---

1. How many unit cubes make up the box below?

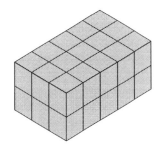

5.MD.3

---

2. Silvano filled a box with unit cubes so that there was no space unfilled. The box had a volume of 514 cubic units. How many unit cubes were in the box?

5.MD.3

---

3. Edna made a rectangular prism that had 10 unit cubes for the width, 7 unit cubes for the length and it had 4 layers. How many unit cubes fit into the prism?

5.MD.3

---

4. How many unit cubes fit in the rectangular prism below?

5.MD.3

---

5. The dog weighs 17 pounds and 8 ounces. The cat weighs 222 ounces. (A) Which animal weighs more and (B) by how much more does it weigh?

5.MD.1

---

6. There will be 11 pounds of corn put evenly into 8 sacks. (A) Write an equation that could be used to find C, the amount of corn each sack will contain. (B) How much corn will be in each sack?

5.NF.3

 **DAY 3**

Volume can be found by multiplying the length by the width by the height.

 **TIP** of the **DAY**

There were 4 different boxes that were filled with unit cubes. The number of cubes used for the width, length and the number of layers are shown. Use this information to answer questions 1 - 3.

Box	Width	Length	Layers
A	11	4	12
B	7	12	8
C	9	10	6
D	12	11	4

1. How many unit cubes were in Box C?

5.MD.3

2. Which box has the most unit cubes in it?

5.MD.3

3. Which 2 boxes can hold the same number of cubes?

5.MD.3

4. How many unit cubes can fit into the rectangular prism below?

5.MD.3

5. Raquel filled a box with unit cubes so that there was no space unfilled. The box had a volume of 112 cubic units. How many unit cubes were in the box?

5.MD.3

6. There were 6 cups of ice cream and each person was to receive $\frac{1}{3}$ cup. (A) Write an equation that could be used to find P, the number of people who can be served the ice cream. (B) How many people can be served with 6 cups of ice cream?

5.NF.7

The volume of a shape represents the number of unit cubes that can fit into that space.

DAY 4

---

1. Sloan had a box that he filled exactly with 815 unit cubes. What was the volume of Sloan's box?

5.MD.3

---

2. How many unit cubes are in the box below?

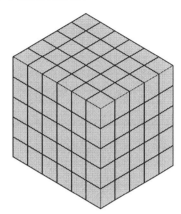

5.MD.3

---

3. Chet made a rectangular prism using unit cubes. He used 6 cubes for the width, 11 cubes for the length and it had 7 layers. How many unit cubes fit into the prism?

5.MD.3

---

4. How many unit cubes are in the prism below?

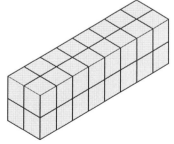

5.MD.3

---

5. What do you know is true about the product of $\frac{2}{3} \times \frac{5}{8}$?

5.NF.5

---

6. Trent was filling a box with unit cubes. He used 12 unit cubes for the width, 9 unit cubes for the length and it had 4 layers. How many unit cubes fit into the box?

5.MD.3

1. How many cubes are in the box below?

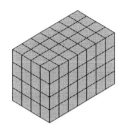

5.MD.3

There were 4 different boxes that were filled with unit cubes. The number of cubes used for the width, length and the number of layers are shown. Use this information to answer questions 2 – 5.

Box	Width	Length	Layers
A	4	6	11
B	12	5	2
C	8	2	12
D	4	3	16

2. Which box holds the fewest cubes?

5.MD.3

3. Which box contains the most cubes?

5.MD.3

4. How many unit cubes were in Box C?

5.MD.3

5. Which 2 boxes have the same number of unit cubes in them?

5.MD.3

6. Sam was making a rectangular prism using unit cubes. He used 15 unit cubes for the width, 12 unit cubes for the length and it had 6 layers. How many unit cubes fit into the prism?

5.MD.3

DAY 6
CHALLENGE QUESTION

One box holds exactly 180 unit cubes. What could its length, width and number of layers be?

5.MD.3

Week 17 goes further into the concept of volume and comparing the volumes of 2 or more figures.

You can find detailed video explanations to each problem in the book by visiting:
ArgoPrep.com

1. Below is a model of Victor's toolbox. What is the volume of the toolbox if each cube is 1 cubic inch?

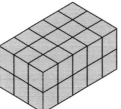

5.MD.4

Figure A is shown below. Each cube in Figure A is 1 m³. Use the drawing to answer questions 2 – 4.

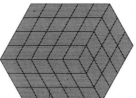

Figure A

2. What is the volume of Figure A?   5.MD.4

3. Figure B has 3 times as many cubes as Figure A. What is the volume of Figure B?   5.MD.4

4. Figure C has half the number of cubes as Figure A. What is the volume of Figure C?   5.MD.4

5. There were 5,817 kilograms of rice that were to be split among 19 food pantries. How many kilograms of rice would each pantry receive?

6. What is the volume of the rectangular prism below if each cube is one cubic foot?

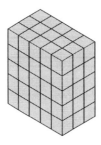

5.MD.4

TIP of the DAY — If there are 216 unit cubes in a space, that space has a volume of 216 cubic units.

DAY 2

Figure D is shown below and each cube is equal to 1 cubic inch. Use the drawing to answer questions 1 – 3.

Figure D

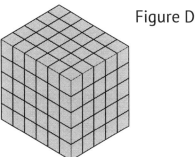

1. What is the volume of Figure D?

5.MD.4

2. Figure E has $\frac{2}{3}$ the number of cubes as Figure D. What is the volume of Figure E?

5.MD.4

3. Figure F has 4 times the number of cubes as Figure D. What is the volume of Figure F?

5.MD.4

Use the rectangular prism shown below to answer questions 4 – 5. Each cube is 1 cm³.

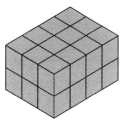

4. What is the volume of the prism?

5.MD.4

5. There is a box that is $\frac{4}{3}$ the size of the prism above. What is the volume of the box?

5.MD.4

6. There was $\frac{1}{3}$ of a gallon of tea left and Sven shared it with his 2 sisters. How much tea did each sibling get?

5.NF.7

DAY 3

Volume is the space an object takes up. A gas can is going to have a larger volume than a juice glass because the gas can takes up more space.

TIP of the DAY

Figure G is shown below. Use it to answer questions 1 – 3.

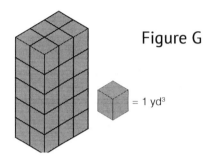

Figure G

= 1 yd³

---

1. What is the volume of Figure G?

5.MD.4

---

2. Figure H has 7 times the number of cubes as Figure G. What is the volume of Figure H?

5.MD.4

---

3. Figure J has $\frac{1}{5}$ the number of cubes as Figure G. What is the volume of Figure J?

5.MD.4

---

4. The blue pen is 12 cm long. The red pen is 72 mm long. What is the difference between the 2 pens?

5.MD.1

---

5. Round 16,382.5107 to the nearest thousand.

5.NBT.4

---

6. What is the value of $300 - 6 \times (20 - 9) \div 2$?

5.OA.1

Figure K is shown below. Use the figure to answer questions 1 – 3.

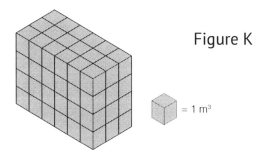

Figure K

= 1 m³

1. What is the volume of Figure K?

   5.MD.4

2. Figure L has a volume that is $\frac{1}{4}$ as large as Figure K. What is the volume of Figure L?

   5.MD.4

3. Figure M has a volume that is twice as large as Figure K. What is the volume of Figure M?

   5.MD.4

4. Write the standard form number for three thousand, five hundred sixteen and two hundredths.

   5.NBT.3

5. What is the volume for the rectangular prism below if each cube is 1 mm³?

   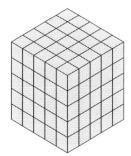

   5.MD.4

6. Nomi had 4,242 bats that he needed to put into boxes that hold 42 bats each. (A) Write an equation that could be used to find *B*, the number of boxes needed. (B) How many boxes would Nomi need?

   5.NBT.6

Below is a rectangular prism. Use the drawing to answer questions 1 – 3.

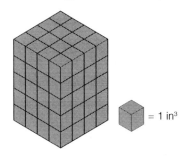

= 1 in³

1. How much space does the rectangular prism occupy?

5.MD.4

2. How much space would 3 of these prisms occupy?

5.MD.4

3. Richa has a box that is $\frac{3}{5}$ as large as the prism above. What is the volume of Richa's box?

5.MD.4

Use the figure below to answer questions 4 – 6.

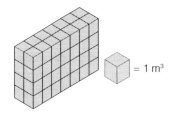

= 1 m³

4. How many cubes are in the rectangular prism above?

5.MD.3

5. If the figure above were laid flat to become the bottom layer of a rectangular prism that had 5 layers, what would the volume of the new rectangular prism be?

5.MD.4

DAY 6
CHALLENGE
QUESTION

There are 3 rectangular prisms that have a TOTAL volume of 726 cubic meters. If there was a box that was $\frac{1}{2}$ the size of one of the original boxes, what would its volume be?

5.MD.5

Volume, volume and more volume problems are found in Week 18. Be sure to use the correct units - some problems talk about area and others talk about volume.

**You can find detailed video explanations to each problem in the book by visiting:
ArgoPrep.com**

---

1. What is the volume of the rectangular prism shown below?

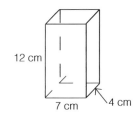

12 cm

7 cm   4 cm

5.MD.5

---

2. There is a pool that is 8 feet deep and the area of the floor of the pool is 294 square feet. How much water would it take to fill that pool?

5.MD.5

---

3. Write a multiplication equation for the model shown below.

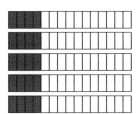

5.NF.3

---

4. The garage had a floor that was 144 square feet and the height of the garage was 12 feet. What was the volume of the garage?

5.MD.5

Use the right rectangular prism below to answer questions 5 – 6.

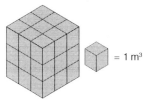

= 1 m³

---

5. What is the volume of the prism?

5.MD.4

---

6. If there was a different prism that had the same volume but a base of only 6 unit cubes, how many layers would the new prism have?

5.MD.4

There are 3 dimensions used to find volume – length, width, and height. The units used to measure volume are also three-dimensional.

DAY 2

---

1. What is the volume of the right rectangular prism shown?

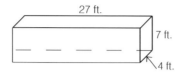

27 ft.

7 ft.

4 ft.

5.MD.5

---

2. What is the volume of the right rectangular prism shown below?

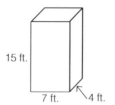

15 ft.

7 ft.   4 ft.

5.MD.5

---

3. If the 2 boxes from #1 and #2 were joined together, what would be the volume of the new shape shown below?

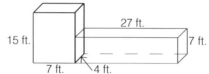

27 ft.

15 ft.   7 ft.

7 ft.   4 ft.

5.MD.5

---

4. What is the volume of the rectangular prism below?

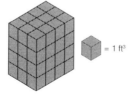

= 1 ft³

5.MD.4

---

5. If the prism from #4 was divided into 3 equal prisms, what would be the volume of one of the "new" prisms?

5.MD.4

---

6. Vance played golf for $4\frac{2}{3}$ hours. Tobey played $1\frac{1}{2}$ times as much as Vance. How many hours did Tobey play golf?

5.NF.6

DAY 3

Volumes can be added together. If Figure A is 95 cm³ and Figure B is 86 cm³, then if Figures A and B were put together, the new volume would be 181 cm³.

TIP of the DAY

---

1. There is a fish tank that is 23 inches deep and the area of the bottom of the tank is 285 inches². How much water will fit in that tank?

5.MD.5

---

2. Figure N has 37 ft³ more volume than the prism below. What is the volume of Figure N?

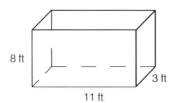

8 ft

3 ft

11 ft

5.MD.5

---

3. Figure A has a length of 8 yards, a width of 7 yards and has 3 layers. Figure B is shown below.

Figure B

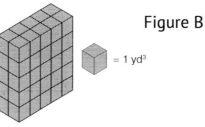

= 1 yd³

Write a number sentence comparing the volumes of Figures A and B.

5.MD.4/5.MD.5

---

4. What is the area of the rectangle shown below?

$\frac{4}{7}$ m

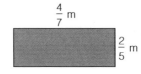

$\frac{2}{5}$ m

5.NF.4

---

5. Sara was adding 12.81 and 764.2. She thought the sum was 892.3. What did Sara most likely forget to do?

5.NBT.7

---

6. Taylor got a cake for his birthday. He ate $\frac{1}{2}$ of it right away, then $\frac{1}{6}$ of it the next day. What fraction of his cake was left?

5.NF.2

Volume can also be calculated by multiplying the area of the base of the prism with the prism's height.

DAY 4

---

1. A right rectangular prism has a volume of 700 cubic inches. If the height is 70 inches, what are the length and width of the rectangular prism?

5.MD.5

---

2. There is a rectangular prism that is completely filled with 728 unit cubes. If there are 8 layers, what are the length and width of the prism?

5.MD.5

---

3. Murphy's fish tank is 16 inches tall and the area of the floor of the tank is 182 in². How much water is in that tank when it is full?

5.MD.5

Use the drawing below to answer questions 4 – 5.

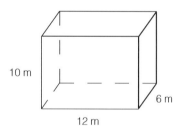

10 m

6 m

12 m

---

4. What is the volume of the prism above?

5.MD.5

---

5. If 3 of the same prisms from #4 were connected together, what would be the volume of the new shape?

5.MD.5

---

6. How many unit cubes are in the rectangular prism below?

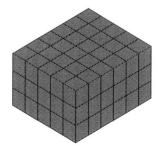

5.MD.3

The figures below are only the bases of right rectangular prisms that all have 11 layers. The first 2 figures are combined to make the third figure. Use the drawing to answer questions 1 – 3.

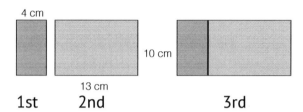

4 cm

10 cm

13 cm

1st   2nd   3rd

1. What is the volume of the first figure?

5.MD.5

2. What is the volume of the second Figure?

5.MD.5

3. The third figure is formed by adding the first 2 together. What is the volume of the third figure?

5.MD.5

The table below has the dimensions for 4 different right rectangular prisms. Use the table to answer questions 4 – 5.

Prism	Length	Width	Height
A	18 in	12 in	5 in
B	10in	11in	8 in
C	15in	5 in	7in
D	11in	14in	6in

4. Which prism has the (A) largest volume? (B) smallest volume?

5.MD.5

5. Which prism would have a volume of 1,848 in^3 if it were doubled?

5.MD.5

 **DAY 6**

CHALLENGE QUESTION

If Prisms A, B, C and D were joined together, what would the combined volume be?

5.MD.5

This week (Week 19) you will learn how to graph points and find the coordinates of points on a graph.

You can find detailed video explanations to each problem in the book by visiting:
ArgoPrep.com

DAY 1

The order of the coordinates of an ordered pair is very important. If the order changes, the location of the point changes.

Use the graph below to answer questions 1 – 5.

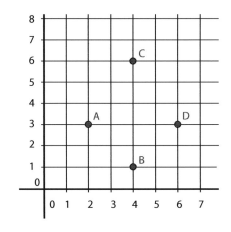

1. What ordered pair is located at Point A?

5.G.1

2. What is the y-coordinate for Point B?

5.G.1

3. Which 2 points have the same y-coordinate?

5.G.1

4. Which 2 points have the same x-coordinate?

5.G.1

5. Which point is located at (4, 6)?

5.G.1

6. How do you know that $\frac{4}{4} \times 10 = 10$?

5.NF.5

The first coordinate in an ordered pair is the x-coordinate. The x-coordinate shows the horizontal distance from the origin.

TIP of the **DAY**

DAY 2

Use the graph below to answer questions 1 – 5.

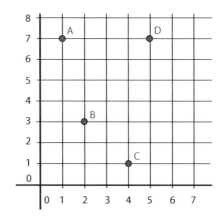

---

1. What are the coordinates for the origin?

5.G.1

---

2. What are the coordinates for Point B?

5.G.1

---

3. Which 2 points have the same y-coordinate?

5.G.1

---

4. Which point is located at $(4, 1)$?

5.G.1

---

5. What is the x-coordinate for Point D?

5.G.1

---

6. Using 14.08 and 10^3, what is their (A) product (B) quotient?

5.NBT.2

DAY 3

The second coordinate in an ordered pair is the y-coordinate. The y-coordinate shows the vertical distance from the origin.

The table and graph below represent 4 trees in a forest. Use the information to answer questions 1 – 4.

Tree	Point on Graph
Aspen	A
Birch	B
Cedar	C
Duck Oak	D

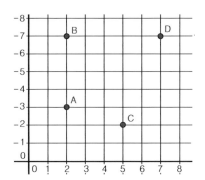

1. Where is the Birch tree located?

5.G.2

2. What is the x-coordinate for the Cedar tree?

5.G.2

3. Write a true statement about the Birch and Duck Oak trees.

5.G.2

4. Which tree is closest to (1, 4)?

5.G.2

5. Zoe used a ribbon that was $13\frac{2}{5}$ cm. Ally used one that was $7\frac{2}{3}$ cm less than Zoe's ribbon. How many cm was Ally's ribbon?

5.NF.1

When using ordered pairs, remember to always start at (0,0).

DAY 4

The table and graph below represent 4 restaurants in a town. Use the information to answer questions 1 – 3.

Restaurant	Point on Graph
Ava's	A
BananaRama	B
Caliente	C
Duffers	D

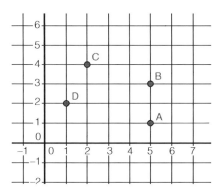

1. Where is Caliente located?

5.G.2

2. The bus line runs along y = 2.
(A) Which restaurant is on the bus line?
(B) Which 2 restaurants are 1 street off of the bus line?

5.G.2

3. (A) Which coordinate do Ava's and BananaRama have in common?
(B) What is the value of that coordinate?

5.G.2

4. What is 28 × 9,106?

5.NBT.5

5. Each month Xander is able to save $\frac{2}{11}$ of the cost of a car. How many months would it take Xander to have enough for a car?

5.NF.5

The table and graph below represent locations of 4 stores in a city. Use the information to answer questions 1 – 4.

Store	Point on Graph
Axed	A
Bernardo's	B
Chime	C
DownTown	D

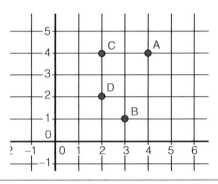

1. Which 2 stores are located the closest to each other?   5.G.2

2. What are the coordinates for Axed?   5.G.2

3. Which store is the furthest from DownTown?   5.G.2

4. A parking lot is located at (1, 4). Which store is closest to the lot?   5.G.2

5. What is the volume of a right rectangular prism that can fit 25 less unitscubes into it than the right rectangular prism shown below?

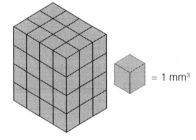

= 1 mm³

5.MD.5

DAY 6

CHALLENGE QUESTION

Point A is located at (2, 6) and Point B is located at (5, 9). What are the coordinates for a point that has the same x-coordinate as Point A and the same y-coordinate as Point B?

5.G.1

Last week - way to go! Week 20 gives lots of exercises to help you understand attributes and traits that are given to specific shapes.

You can find detailed video explanations to each problem in the book by visiting:
ArgoPrep.com

DAY 1

Shapes may fit into more than one category or be able to be described in different ways. For example, a rectangle is both a quadrilateral and a parallelogram.

Use the drawing below to answer questions 1 – 4.

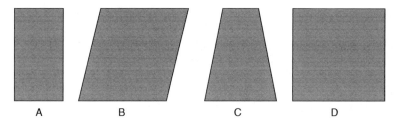

A   B   C   D

---

1. What category do ALL 4 shapes belong to?

5.G.3

---

2. To what categories do both A and B belong?

5.G.3

---

3. Which shape is NOT a parallelogram?

5.G.3

---

4. Which shape/s are rectangles?

5.G.3

---

5. What shape has 5 sides?

5.G.3

---

6. What is true about ALL rectangles?

5.G.3

You are almost finished with this workbook – keep it up!

Use the drawing below to answer questions 1 – 4.

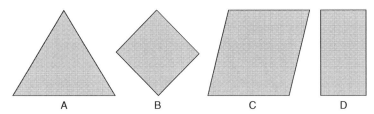

A   B   C   D

---

1. Which of the shapes are parallelograms?

5.G.3

---

2. Which of the shapes appear to be equilateral?

5.G.3

---

3. Besides quadrilateral, to which categories do BOTH B and C belong?

5.G.3

---

4. Which shape does NOT have any parallel sides?

5.G.3

---

5. (A) Describe an isosceles triangle. (B) Draw an isosceles triangle.

5.G.3

---

6. Will has a shape that has 8 sides and 4 pairs of parallel lines. What is Will's shape?

5.G.3

DAY 3

When a description says "EXACTLY" that means no more and no less. So if there are EXACTLY 2 pairs of equal angles, there are 2, NOT 1 or 3 pairs, there are only TWO pairs.

1. There is a quadrilateral that has 4 equal sides but no right angles What is the shape?

5.G.4

2. There is a quadrilateral that has exactly 1 pair of parallel lines. What is the shape?

5.G.4

3. What quadrilateral is not a square but has 4 right angles and opposite sides that are equal?

5.G.4

4. A quadrilateral has 2 pairs of parallel lines, right angles and all sides are equal. What shape is being described?

5.G.4

5. Yvette had a shape that had EXACTLY 3 equal sides. What shape did Yvette have?

5.G.4

6. What is the value of $57\frac{1}{5} - 38\frac{4}{8}$?

5.NF.1

 **TIP** of the **DAY**

Before taking any assessments that include shapes, review the attributes of categories and what traits make up specific shapes.

 **DAY 4**

1. To which category do trapezoids, kites and squares belong?

5.G.4

2. There is a quadrilateral that has 4 equal sides but no right angles. What shape is this quadrilateral?

5.G.4

3. What quadrilateral has EXACTLY 1 pair of parallel lines?

5.G.4

4. (A) Describe a parallelogram. (B) List 3 shapes that are parallelograms.

5.G.4

5. How many $\frac{1}{4}$ quarts are in 16 quarts?

5.NF.7

6. There is a bag of plums that weighs 6 pounds and 8 ounces. There is also a bag of peaches that weighs 120 ounces. (A) Which bag weighs more? (B) How much heavier is that fruit?

5.MD.1

1. Figure A has 3 angles and 1 of them is a right angle. What shape is Figure A?

5.G.4

Use the drawing below to answer questions 2 −4.

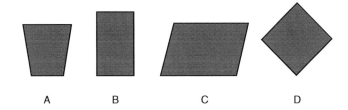

A   B   C   D

2. Which shape has only 1 pair of parallel lines?

5.G.3

3. Which shape is NOT a parallelogram?

5.G.3

4. To which category do ALL of the shapes above belong?

5.G.3

5. What do rectangles and squares (A) have in common (B) NOT have in common?

5.G.4

6. Abraham uses $6\frac{1}{4}$ pounds of butter to make 5 pound cakes. How many pounds of butter would be needed for $7\frac{1}{2}$ cakes?

5.NF.4

 # DAY 6
CHALLENGE
QUESTION

List all of the attributes that rectangles and rhombuses have in common.

5.G.4

THE END!

Assessment

The table below shows the location of some items in a grocery store and the point that corresponds to each item. Use the table and graph below to answer questions 1 – 3.

Avocados	A
Bread	B
Cheese	C
Donuts	D
Eggs	E

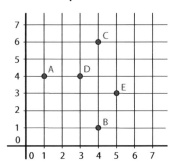

1. What are the coordinates for the cheese?

5.G.1

2. Which 2 items have the same y-coordinate?

5.G.2

3. The stock room is at $(3, 1)$ on the graph. Which item is closest to the stock room?

5.G.1

Figure A is shown below. Each cube in Figure A is 1 cm³. Use the drawing to answer questions 4 – 5.

Figure A

 = 1 cm³

4. What is the volume of Figure A?

5.MD.4

5. Figure B has 3 times MORE cubes than Figure A. What is the volume of Figure B?

5.MD.4

6. Looking at the shapes below, list ALL of the categories that they BOTH belong to.

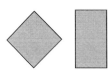

4.OA.5

7. The bus drove 8 kilometers while the train traveled 9,035 meters. Which vehicle traveled farther and by how much?

5.MD.1

8. Alyse thought that $\frac{2}{3} + \frac{1}{4}$ equaled $\frac{2}{12}$. How do you know this answer is incorrect?

5.NF.2

9. If a number is multiplied by 10^5, which direction does the decimal point move and how many places does it move?

5.NBT.2

10. The number 4.391 is given. In a different number, the 3 represents a value which is one-tenth of the value of the 3 in 4.391. What value is represented by the 3 in the other number?

5.NBT.1

11. If Lexie and her 2 sisters each ate a $\frac{5}{3}$ of a peach, how many peaches were there to start with?

5.NF.3

12. What is $50 - 31\frac{1}{4}$?

5.NF.1

13. Forty-two bicycles weigh 381 pounds. The number of pounds per bicycle is between what 2 numbers?

5.NF.3

The table below shows the cost of some watermelons. Use the table to answer questions 14 – 15.

Watermelons	Cost (dollars)
2	10
3	15
5	25

14. What is the cost for 4 watermelons?

5.OA.3

15. What would you expect the cost of 9 watermelons to be?

5.OA.3

16. What place value can be put in the blank to make the statement true?

5.NBT.1

7,000,000 = 70 _____

17. What are all of the categories that BOTH shapes below belong to?

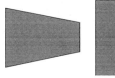

5.G.3

18. The shaded part of the square below has a length of $\frac{3}{4}$ cm and a width of $\frac{2}{3}$ cm.

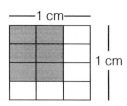

——1 cm——

1 cm

What is the area, in square centimeters, of the shaded part of the square?

5.NF.4

19. How many unit cubes are in the box shown below?

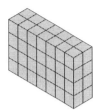

5.MD.3

20. There is a kiddie pool that is 1.5 meters deep and the area of the floor of the pool is 13 square meters. How much water would it take to fill that pool? 5.MD.5

21. What is the value of the expression below?

$$173 + 2 \times (10 + [6 \div 2]) - 47$$

5.OA.1

22. Write in standard form the number that is equal to fourteen thousand, three hundred six and seven hundredths. 5.NBT.3

Use the rectangular prisms shown below to answer questions 23 – 25.
Figure A + Figure B = Figure C and each cube equals 1 cubic inch.

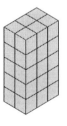  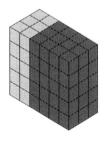

Figure A   Figure B   Figure C

23. What is the volume of Figure A?

5.MD.4

24. What is the volume of Figure B?

5.MD.4

25. What is the volume of Figure C?

5.MD.5

---

26. The Golden Retriever weighed 78 pounds and 3 ounces. How many ounces did the dog weigh?

5.MD.1

---

27. Write a mathematical expression that is equivalent to the number sentence below.

Multiply nine by the sum of three and ten.

5.OA.2

---

28. What is the value of the expression: $12 \div \frac{1}{4}$?

5.NF.7

---

29. There will be $915 worth of jewelry placed evenly into 10 display cases. What is the value of the jewelry (as a fraction) placed in each case?

5.NF.3

---

30. What is 12.095 rounded to the nearest hundredth?

5.NBT.4

---

31. Sofia cut a 48-foot piece of twine into 15 equal pieces for wrapping gifts. How long was each piece of twine?

A. $3\frac{1}{5}$ feet

B. $3\frac{3}{5}$ feet

C. $3\frac{1}{15}$ feet

D. $3\frac{12}{15}$ feet

5.NF.3

32. Which statement is true about the values of the two expressions below?

Expression A: $(17 - 9)$
Expression B: $(17 - 9) + 6$

- **A.** The value of expression A is 6 times the value of Expression B.
- **B.** The value of expression B is 6 times the value of Expression A.
- **C.** The value of Expression A is 6 more than the value of Expression B.
- **D.** The value of Expression B is 6 more than the value of Expression A.

5.OA.2

33. Which expression is the same as 9×10^4?

- **A.** 900,000
- **B.** 90,000
- **C.** 9,000
- **D.** 900

5.NBT.2

34. Which statement is true about the product of $\dfrac{4}{5} \times \dfrac{7}{3}$?

- **A.** The product is greater than each factor.
- **B.** The product is less than each factor.
- **C.** The product is greater than $\dfrac{4}{5}$ but less than $\dfrac{7}{3}$.
- **D.** The product is equal to one of the factors.

5.NF.5

35. Which shape does NOT have at least 2 pairs of parallel lines?

- **A.** rhombus
- **B.** parallelogram
- **C.** rectangle
- **D.** trapezoid

5.G.3

ASSESSMENT

Use the dot plot below to answer questions 36 - 37. It shows some data about rainfall amounts.

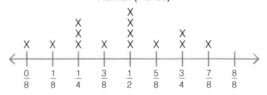

36. How many days of rainfall were recorded?

    A. 10

    B. 12

    C. 14

    D. 15

5.MD.2

37. What was the total rainfall amount recorded?

    A. $5\frac{1}{2}$ inches   **B.** $5\frac{7}{8}$ inches

    C. $6\frac{1}{8}$ inches   **D.** $6\frac{1}{4}$ inches

5.MD.2

38. Which scenario could be described by the model below?

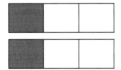

    A. Brooks ate 2 eggs for 3 weeks.

    B. Clara drank $\frac{1}{3}$ gallon of tea on 2 different days.

    C. Dylan ran $\frac{1}{2}$ minute on 3 different days.

    D. Riley worked $\frac{1}{3}$ of an hour on 3 different days.

5.NF.4

39. $11\frac{1}{4} + 23\frac{7}{8} = ?$

    A. $35\frac{1}{8}$ **B.** $35\frac{1}{4}$

    C. $35\frac{1}{2}$ **D.** $35\frac{5}{8}$

5.NF.1

---

40. There are two number patterns below.

      Pattern A: 0, 1, 2, 3, 4...
      Pattern B: 0, 2, 4, 6, 8...

Which statement is true about the patterns above?

    A. All of the numbers in the 2 patterns are different.
    B. All of the numbers in Pattern B can be found in Pattern A.
    C. The 5th number in Pattern B is 2 times as large as the 6th number in Pattern B.
    D. The numbers in Pattern B are half the value of the numbers in Pattern A.

5.OA.3

---

41. Which statement about parallelograms is NOT true?

    A. Rectangles are parallelograms.
    B. Rhombuses are parallelograms.
    C. Opposite sides on a parallelogram are equal.
    D. Parallelograms have 4 right angles.

5.G.3

---

42. Which equation is shown by the model below?

    A. 8 + 6 = 48
    B. 8 × 6 = 56
    C. 48 − 8 = 40
    D. 48 ÷ 6 = 8

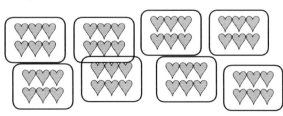

5.NBT.6

43. Wallis drove for $1\frac{7}{8}$ hours and then Aubra drove $2\frac{1}{3}$ times as long. Which equation could be used to find out how many hours Aubra drove?

A. $1\frac{7}{8} \times 2\frac{1}{3} = 4\frac{1}{8}$

B. $1\frac{7}{8} \times 2\frac{1}{3} = 4\frac{3}{8}$

C. $1\frac{7}{8} \times 2\frac{1}{3} = 4\frac{3}{24}$

D. $1\frac{7}{8} \times 2\frac{1}{3} = 4\frac{5}{8}$

5.NF.6

44. Which ordered pair can be found by starting at the origin and then moving 3 units to the right on the x-axis and 7 units up on the y-axis?

A. $(3, 7)$

B. $(7, 3)$

C. $(3x, 7y)$

D. $(3/7)$

5.G.1

45. Which number is the product of 706 and 98?

A. 7,448

B. 68,448

C. 69,188

D. 74,488

5.NBT.5

46. Which equation is NOT shown in the model below?

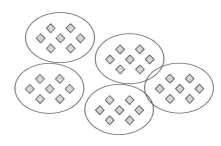

  A. 7 + 5 = 12
  B. 7 × 5 = 35
  C. 35 ÷ 5 = 7
  D. 5 × 7 = 35

5.NBT.6

---

47. Which equation can be used to find the value of the expression below?

$$2.53 + 61.7$$

  A. 64.23 ÷ 2.53 = 61.7
  B. 64.23 – 2.53 = 61.7
  C. 61.7 + 2.53 = 87.0
  D. 87.0 – 61.7 = 2.53

5.NBT.7

---

48. The results of a survey of 5th graders who take music lessons are shown below.

Flute	$\frac{1}{3}$
Guitar	$\frac{1}{4}$
Clarinet	$\frac{1}{8}$

What fraction of the 5th graders play something OTHER than the 3 instruments listed?

  A. $\frac{1}{5}$ **B.** $\frac{7}{24}$

  C. $\frac{17}{24}$ **D.** $\frac{12}{15}$

5.NF.2

ANSWER KEYS

VIDEO EXPLANATIONS

ARGOPREP.COM

ANSWER KEY

**For more practice with 5th Grade Math, be sure to check out our other book,
Common Core Math Workbook Grade 5: Multiple Choice**

WEEK 1

Day 1
1. **A.** 10 times **B.** 100 times
2. $\frac{1}{10}$
3. **A.** Any number that has a 6 in the tens place is correct. Examples: 64 or 13,469
B. Any number that has a 6 in the thousands place is correct. Examples: 6,000 or 6,432
4. two tenths
5. $\frac{1}{100}$
6. 100 times

Day 2
1. Answers will vary but any number that has a 3 in the thousands place is correct. Examples: 13,590 or 3,472.
2. $\frac{1}{100}$ times
3. Sunday
4. Friday
5. Wednesday

Day 3
1. seven hundredths
2. $\frac{1}{100}$
3. 1,000 times
4. ten thousands
5. **A.** Any number that has a 5 in the tens place is correct. Examples: 154 or 1,659
B. Any number that has a 5 in the hundred thousands place is correct Examples: 516,294 or 580,473
6. 100

Day 4
1. 10
2. hundred thousands
3. **A.** 137.6 **B.** 1,376
C. 13,760
4. 230,000
5. **A.** 34.916 **B.** 3.4916
C. 0.34916
6. **A.** 10^5 **B.** 10^2

Day 5
1. $\frac{1}{10}$
2. hundred thousands
3. 41.9
4. **A.** 73,450.8
B. 734,508
C. 73,450,800
5. 7,000,000
6. **A.** 0.12769
B. 0.012769
C. 0.0012769
Answers will vary. Any number that has an 8 in the hundreds place is correct. Examples: 812 or 116,842

Week 2

Day 1
1. 92,000
2. **A.** 180.3
B. 18,030
3. 400
4. hundreds
5. **A.** 0.065129
B. 6.5129
6. 904

Day 2
1. hundred thousands
2. 159.28
3. 95,681.025
4. **A.** 3,110.08 **B.** $(3 \times 1000) + (1 \times 100) +$
$(1 \times 10) + \left(8 \times \frac{1}{100}\right)$
5. **A.** $(3 \times 100) + (5 \times 10) + (4 \times 1) + \left(1 \times \frac{1}{10}\right)$
$+ \left(9 \times \frac{1}{1000}\right)$
B. three hundred fifty-four and one hundred nine thousandths
6. 0.12 < 12 hundreds or 12 hundreds > 0.12

Day 3
1. **A.** seventeen thousand, eight hundred ninety-two and one tenth
B. 1(10,000) + 7(1,000) + 8(100) + 9(10) + 2(1) + 1$\left(\frac{1}{10}\right)$
2. 20,000
3. 86.7, 86.79, 86.94, 86.97
4. 5370.602
5. **A.** 7,014.02
B. 7(1,000) + 1(10) + 4(1) + 2$\left(\frac{1}{100}\right)$
6. eight thousandths

Day 4
1. **A.** three hundred sixty and two hundred eighty-one thousandths
B. $(3 \times 100) + (6 \times 10) + \left(2 \times \frac{1}{10}\right) + \left(8 \times \frac{1}{100}\right) + \left(1 \times \frac{1}{1000}\right)$
2. 79.2543
3. 313.975, 314.78, 314.807, 314.9
4. **A.** 16,209.12
B. $(1 \times 10,000) + (6 \times 1,000) + (2 \times 100) + (9 \times 1) + \left(1 \times \frac{1}{10}\right) + \left(2 \times \frac{1}{100}\right)$
5. 17.9 > 17.869 or 17.869 < 17.9
6. 6.107, 6.14, 6.143, 6.2

Day 5
1. four hundredths
2. 563.8042
3. 240.999, 241.68, 241.7, 241.705
4. **A.** 400,826.005
B. $(4 \times 100,000) + (8 \times 100) + (2 \times 10) + (6 \times 1) + \left(5 \times \frac{1}{1000}\right)$
5. 35.8 = 35.800 or 35.800 = 35.8
6. 726.875, 726.9, 726.91, 726.95

Week 3

Day 1
1. **A.** 2.9 **B.** 2.92 **C.** 2.915
2. 21.24
3. Answers will vary. Any number that has a 9 in the thousandths place is correct. Examples: 0.009 or 41.3891
4. **A.** 784.4 **B.** 800
5. 3,000
6. 294.719

Day 2
1. 729.1 inches
2. DBAC
3. 182.37 < 182.4 or 182.4 > 182.37
4. **A.** 4,506.4 **B.** 4,506.389
5. 4344.68

Day 3
1. 1,564
2. 125,433
3. **A.** $4,125 **B.** $1,374 **C.** $888
4. $25,548
5. The decimal point is moved 6 places to the left.

Day 4
1. 1,401,972
2. 886.63
3. 100
4. 628,940
5. 5.8706
6. 2,034,747

Day 5
1. 1079.52
2. **A.** 915.0 **B.** 915.00 **C.** 914.997
3. **A.** 5,689,500 **B.** 5,690,000 **C.** 5,700,000
4. 476,800
5. **A.** nine hundred forty-two and fifty-one hundredths
B. $(9 \times 100) + (4 \times 10) + (2 \times 1) + \left(5 \times \frac{1}{10}\right) + \left(1 \times \frac{1}{100}\right)$
6. 320,540

Week 4

Day 1
1. 30 ÷ 6 = 5 or 5 × 6 = 30 or 30 ÷ 5 = 6 or 6 × 5 = 30
2. 461
3. 214
4. 387
5. 100 times
6. 84 ÷ 14 = 6 or 14 × 6 = 84 or 84 ÷ 6 = 14 or 6 × 14 = 84

Day 2
1. 516
2. 99
3. 91 ÷ 13 = 7 or 13 × 7 = 91 or 91 ÷ 7 = 13 or 7 × 13 = 84
4. one tenth
5. 208
6. 283

Day 3
1. **A.** 242 **B.** 605
2. 83.11
3. 383.624
4. ten thousands
5. 168.1
6. 1906.43

Day 4
1. 767.06 cannot be the sum because 980.6 > 767.06 so the sum should also be > 980.6.
2. $39.01
3. 11.8
4. 159.6
5. 1,593 km
6. **A.** nine thousand, six hundred forty-five and eight tenths
B. $(9 \times 1000) + (6 \times 100) + (4 \times 10) + (5 \times 1) + \left(8 \times \frac{1}{10}\right)$

Day 5
1. **A.** 138.84 **B.** 14.6
2. 219.4 pounds
3. **A.** 130.2 **B.** 1134.88
4. 57
5. 26.3
6. 99.3

Week 5

Day 1
1. 8
2. 12
3. 305
4. 630
5. **A.** 60,000 **B.** sixty thousand
6. The product of three and the sum of seven and five or three times the sum of seven and five

Day 2
1. 181
2. Three more than the product of five and eight
3. 80
4. Eleven less than the product of eight and seven
5. **A.** 9,293.39 **B.** 8,208.61
6. **A.** 4213.7 **B.** 4213.715

Day 3
1. 29
2. Twelve more than the quotient of fifteen and three
3. **A.** 7,290 **B.** 1,000
4. 56,416
5. 101
6. The sum of nineteen and eleven, divided by ten

Day 4
1. The value of Expression A is 7 less than the value of Expression B or the value of Expression B is 7 more than the value of Expression A.
2. (35 + 7) × 4
3. **A.** Seven thousand, five hundred forty-three and six hundredths
B. 7,543.06
4. The value of expression A is 10 times the value of Expression B or the value of expression B is $\frac{1}{10}$ the value of Expression A.
5. 3 × (6 + 11)
6. $\frac{1}{10}$

Day 5
1. 238
2. 105
3. (21 + 8) ÷ 9
4. The value of Expression A is 3 more than the value of Expression B or the value of Expression B is 3 less than the value of Expression A.
5. **A.** 6,080 **B.** 0.00608
6. **A.** Four hundred seventy-one and five tenths
B. $(4 \times 100) + (7 \times 10) + (1 \times 1) + \left(5 \times \frac{1}{10}\right)$

Week 6

Day 1
1. $(9 \times 6) - 2$
2. The value of expression A is 4 times the value of Expression B or the value of expression B is $\frac{1}{4}$ the value of Expression A.
3. $5 + (14 \times 2)$ or $(14 \times 2) + 5$
4. $(75 \div 5) + 9$
5. The value of Expression A is 8 less than the value of Expression B or the value of Expression B is 8 more than the value of Expression A.
6. Any number that has a 3 in the hundreds place is correct. Examples: 340 or 107,356

Day 2
1. Four times the difference between 19 and 7
2. 14
3. The value of expression A is 8 times the value of Expression B or the value of expression B is $\frac{1}{8}$ the value of Expression A.
4. $2 \times (12 - 5)$
5. A. $39.75   B. $48.16
6. A. Nine thousand, seventy-one and five hundredths

   B. $(9 \times 1000) + (7 \times 10) + (1 \times 1) + \left(5 \times \frac{1}{100}\right)$

Day 3
1. Twelve less than the product of ten and six.
2. The numbers in Pattern A are 1 more than the numbers in Pattern B or the numbers in Pattern B are 1 less than the numbers in Pattern A.
3. $9
4. $30
5. A. 17,300   B. 17,325.10

Day 4
1. Pattern A is 3 times as many as Pattern B or Pattern B is $\frac{1}{3}$ as many as Pattern A.
2. Day 3
3. 15
4. 18
5. five tenths

Day 5
1. $16 + (9 \times 2)$ or $(9 \times 2) + 16$
2. A. $20   B. $32
3. T-shirts cost $4 each so the number of shirts times 4 is the cost.
4. The values in Pattern B are twice the values as Pattern A or the values in Pattern A are half the values of Pattern B.
5. $9 \times 4 = 36$ or $36 \div 4 = 9$

Week 7

Day 1
1. $16 \frac{1}{20}$
2. $32 \frac{5}{9}$
3. $\frac{25}{28}$
4. $18 \frac{5}{6}$
5. 300,000
6. 15

Day 2
1. $60 \frac{8}{15}$
2. $107 \frac{3}{8}$
3. $\frac{1}{8}$
4. $8 \frac{1}{10}$
5. 113
6. A. 25.0   B. 25.020

Day 3
1. $15 \frac{1}{7}$
2. $49 \frac{5}{8}$
3. $47 \frac{7}{40}$
4. 140,060
5. $1 \frac{5}{24}$
6. $121 \frac{4}{9}$

Day 4
1. $101 \frac{7}{22}$
2. $66 \frac{8}{15}$
3. $30 \frac{5}{6}$
4. $1 \frac{7}{12}$
5. $\frac{1}{10}$
6. A. $(2 \times 1000) + (6 \times 100) + (9 \times 10) + (4 \times 1) + \left(5 \times \frac{1}{10}\right) + \left(3 \times \frac{1}{1000}\right)$

   B. Two thousand, six hundred ninety-four and five hundred three thousandths

Day 5
1. $30 \frac{9}{10}$
2. $909 \frac{5}{8}$
3. A. $141 \frac{3}{7}$ B. $58 \frac{4}{7}$
4. A. 21.505   B. 64.67235
5. A. 312,950,000   B. 312.95

Week 8

Day 1
1. A. $D = 1 - \frac{3}{4}$ B. It did not rain for $\frac{1}{4}$ of the trip.
2. $\frac{7}{24}$
3. $\frac{7}{12}$
4. $\frac{5}{24}$ of a mile
5. 265,396

Day 2
1. $\frac{7}{12}$
2. $\frac{1}{24}$
3. $\frac{5}{24}$
4. 2/3 > 3/7 so anything added to 2/3 should also be > 3/7
5. A. $(6 \times 10) + (9 \times 1) + \left(2 \times \frac{1}{10}\right) + \left(3 \times \frac{1}{100}\right)$

   B. Sixty-nine and twenty-three hundredths

Day 3
1. $13 \frac{1}{24}$
2. $9 \frac{17}{20}$
3. $10 \frac{4}{9}$
4. $4 \frac{3}{5}$
5. A. 105   B. 488.8

Day 4
1. $\frac{1}{18}$
2. $\frac{5}{18}$
3. $\frac{5}{6}$
4. A. 16.4 and 16.40
   B. 16.4 = 16.40 or 16.40 = 16.4
5. nine ones

Day 5
1. $\frac{8}{15}$
2. $\frac{7}{30}$
3. $\frac{11}{30}$
4. 527 miles
5. $\frac{7}{12}$

Week 9

Day 1
1. A. $T = 3 \div 16$ B. Each person will receive $\frac{3}{16}$ gallons
2. A. $F = 10 \div 7$ B. $1 \frac{3}{7}$ pounds of flour/sack
3. 3
4. 24
5. A. $S = 10 \div 3$ B. $3 \frac{1}{3}$
6. $7 \frac{1}{5}$ feet

Day 2
1. A. $C = 850 \div 30$ B. $28 \frac{1}{3}$ servings
2. $138 \frac{8}{9}$
3. $23 \frac{2}{9}$
4. A. $C = 84 \div 30$ B. $2 \frac{4}{5}$
5. $\frac{5}{8}$
6. 713.924

Day 3
1. 14
2. $3 \frac{3}{5}$
3. $10 \frac{2}{5}$
4. 5
5. $\frac{1}{6}$

Day 4
1. $99 \frac{5}{7}$
2. A. $R = 15 \div 24$ B. $\frac{5}{8}$ kg of rice
3. $14 \frac{3}{4}$
4. 11
5. 10

Day 5
1. $6 \frac{1}{6}$
2. $6 \frac{1}{3}$
3. A. $R = 12 \div 5$ B. $2 \frac{2}{5}$
4. The value of Expression A is 8 less than the value of Expression B or the value of Expression B is 8 more than the value of Expression A.
5. $2 \frac{1}{5}$ feet
6. A. $B = 51 \div 17$ B. 3

Week 10

Day 1
1. A. $A = \frac{1}{2} \times \frac{6}{7}$ B. $\frac{3}{7}$ in^2
2. $\frac{2}{3} \times 4 = \frac{8}{3} = 2 \frac{2}{3}$
3. $(9 \times 12) - 8$
4. $\frac{18}{35}$ square meters
5. A. Models may vary but may look something like this:
   B. $\frac{4}{7}$
6. $\frac{4}{15} \times 5 = \frac{20}{15} = \frac{4}{3}$

Day 2
1. $\frac{2}{4} \times \frac{2}{7} = \frac{4}{28} = \frac{1}{7}$
2. A. $A = \frac{4}{5} \times \frac{2}{9}$ B. $\frac{8}{45}$ m^2
3. $\frac{3}{20}$
4. A. $A = \frac{3}{4} \times \frac{3}{5}$
   B. $\frac{9}{20}$ yd^2
5. $1 \frac{1}{9}$ m^2
6. $\frac{1}{2} \times 6 = 3$

Day 3
1. A. $A = \frac{4}{7} \times \frac{5}{6}$ B. $\frac{10}{21}$ ft^2
2. $\frac{4}{5} \times 6 = \frac{24}{5}$
3. 9-10
4. $15
5. $45
6. $\frac{1}{2}$ in^2

Day 4
1. A. $A = \frac{5}{6} \times \frac{2}{5}$ B. $\frac{1}{3}$ square meters
2. 104-105
3. $\frac{9}{20}$ yds^2
4. $\frac{2}{3} \times \frac{5}{6} = \frac{5}{9}$
5. $\frac{8}{21}$
6. $\frac{8}{15}$ yd^2

Day 5
1. A. Answers may vary but may look something like:

   B. $\frac{4}{40}$ or $\frac{1}{10}$
2. $\frac{12}{35}$ yd^2
3. 8-9
4. $\frac{7}{96}$ mm^2
5. Pattern B has values that are 3 times the values in Pattern A or Pattern A has values that are one-third the values of Pattern B.
6. $\frac{3}{4} \times 5 = \frac{15}{4}$

143

Week 11

Day 1
1. Answers will vary but may include: The product is greater than both factors because each factor is less than one so the product should be greater than either factor.
2. 5 pay periods
3. Answers may vary but should be something like: $\frac{1}{6}$ is less than 1, so when a number is multiplied by 1/6, the product should be less than that number. Diagrams may include 8 sets of $\frac{1}{6}$ and may look like the model shown here (times 8).

4. Answers may vary but can include: The product is equal to 12 because $\frac{8}{8} = 1$ and $1 \times 12 = 12$.
5. 7 days
6. Any fraction that has a numerator that is smaller than the denominator will work.

Day 2
1. Answers may vary but should be something like: $\frac{7}{4}$ is greater than 1 so $\frac{7}{4} \times 5 > 5$. Diagrams may include 5 sets of $\frac{7}{4}$ and may look like the model shown here (times 5).
2. A. 4 months   B. exactly enough with no extra
3. Answers may vary but can include: The product is equal to 9 because $\frac{4}{4} = 1$ and $1 \times 9 = 9$.
4. A. 3 months   B. there will be extra
5. Answers may vary but should include that the product is greater than $\frac{7}{8}$ but less than 18.
6. $5\frac{2}{3}$

Day 3
1. 8 minutes
2. Answers will vary but any fraction that has the a numerator that is larger than the denominator will work. Examples: $\frac{10}{9}, \frac{7}{6}, \frac{5}{3}$
3. Answers may vary but should include that the product is greater than $\frac{4}{9}$ but less than 11.
4. $\frac{4}{5}$ is less than 1 so $10 \times \frac{4}{5}$ should be < 10. Diagrams may include 10 sets of $\frac{4}{5}$ and may look like the model shown here (times 10).

5. 455,532
6. 5 weeks

Day 4
1. 7 hours
2. Answers may vary but should be something like: $\frac{5}{5} = 1$ so $4 \times \frac{5}{5} = 4 \times 1 = 4$. Diagrams may include 4 sets of $\frac{5}{5}$ and may look like the model shown here. (times 4)
3. Answers may vary but should include that the product is greater than $\frac{1}{7}$ but less than 9.
4. 395
5. Answers may vary but any fraction that has the same numerator and denominator will work. Examples: $\frac{9}{9}, \frac{4}{4}, \frac{13}{13}$
6. Answers may vary but should be something like: $\frac{3}{2} > 1$ so $\frac{3}{2} \times 3$ > 3. Diagrams may include 3 sets of $\frac{3}{2}$ and may look like the model shown here (times 3).

Day 5
1. Answers may vary but can include:
The product is equal to 7 because $\frac{3}{3} = 1$ and $1 \times 7 = 7$.
2. Answers will vary but any fraction that has a numerator smaller than the denominator will work. Examples: $\frac{1}{4}$, $\frac{7}{10}, \frac{5}{6}$
3. Answers will vary but should include something about the product is less than both $\frac{3}{5}$ and $\frac{2}{9}$ because both fractions are < 1. When a number is multiplied by a fraction < 1, the product is less than the original number.
4. 5 hours
5. Answers may vary but should be something like: $\frac{9}{9} = 1$ so $15 \times \frac{9}{9} = 15 \times 1$ = 15. Diagrams may include 15 sets of $\frac{9}{9}$ and may look like the model shown here (times 15).
6. A. Answers will vary but it could look something like this:
B. $\frac{6}{5}$ hours or $1\frac{1}{5}$ hours

Week 12

Day 1
1. A. $J = 3\frac{1}{5} \times \frac{1}{2}$ B. $1\frac{3}{5}$
2. $3\frac{1}{5}$ hours
3. $11\frac{3}{4}$ hours
4. $1\frac{1}{2}$ hours
5. $\frac{7}{5} > 1$ and $\frac{4}{3} > 1$ so the product of these 2 factors will be greater than either of them.
6. $\frac{5}{6}$

Day 2
1. Ham/Cheese
2. Pastrami
3. A. 12 kg   B. 19 kg   C. 7 kg
4. $5\frac{13}{15}$
5. A. $J = 12\frac{3}{5} \times \frac{7}{9}$ B. $\frac{49}{5} = 9\frac{4}{5}$ km

Day 3
1. A. $K = 10\frac{1}{5} \times \frac{2}{3}$ B. $\frac{34}{5} = 6\frac{4}{5}$
2. $2\frac{1}{4}$
3. $7\frac{1}{2}$
4. $13\frac{1}{2}$
5. $\frac{8}{15}$ yd²
6. 7-8

Day 4
1. Jolene
2. 5
3. A. 4 miles   B. $5\frac{3}{5}$ miles
4. $6\frac{1}{4}$
5. A. $M = 14\frac{1}{5} \times \frac{3}{4}$ B. $10\frac{13}{20}$
6. $(11 \times 4) - 13$

Day 5
1. $18\frac{2}{3}$
2. A. $K = 2\frac{4}{5} \times \frac{1}{2}$ B. $1\frac{2}{5}$
3. 7 meters
4. A. 5413.782   B. 541.3782   C. 54.13782
5. A. $N = 3\frac{1}{4} \times 3$ B. $9\frac{3}{4}$ hours
6. 73.9, 74.089, 74.152, 74.16

Week 13

Day 1
1. $\frac{1}{27}$
2. A. $P = \frac{1}{4} \div 5$ B. $\frac{1}{20}$
3. 50
4. A. $P = \frac{1}{2} \div 3$ B. $\frac{1}{6}$
5. A. $C = 5 \div \frac{1}{5}$ B. 25 candies
6. A. $\frac{23}{24}$ B. $\frac{7}{24}$

Day 2
1. 28
2. 96
3. A. $C = \frac{1}{3} \div 2$ B. $\frac{1}{6}$
4. 36
5. 72
6. A. $S = 16 \div 4$ B. 4

Day 3
1. $\frac{1}{6}$
2. $\frac{1}{12}$
3. $\frac{1}{8}$
4. $\frac{7}{10}$
5. A. 12,738   B. 0.012738
6. 381

Day 4
1. 20
2. $\frac{1}{6}$ mile
3. 24
4. A. $A = \frac{1}{9} \div 3$ B. $\frac{1}{27}$
5. 121.8
6. Answers may vary but any number between (and including) 8,095 – 8,149 is correct.

Day 5
1. $\frac{1}{8}$
2. 21
3. A. $P = \frac{1}{8} \div 4$ B. $\frac{1}{32}$
4. 60
5. Answers will vary but as long as the fraction has a larger numerator than denominator, it is correct. Examples: $\frac{11}{4}, \frac{6}{3}, \frac{9}{8}$.
6. $\frac{1}{8}$

Week 14

Day 1
1. A. Lindsay   B. 93 meters
2. A. Oskar's cousin   B. 13
3. 37
4. 148
5. A. seventy-two thousand, three hundred eight and sixteen thousandths
B. $(7 \times 10,000) + (2 \times 1,000) + (3 \times 100) + (8 \times 1) + \left(1 \times \frac{1}{100}\right) + \left(6 \times \frac{1}{1000}\right)$
6. A. Mia   B. 6723 m or 6.723 km

Day 2
1. A. Chimpanzee   B. Penguin
2. 26 pounds, 11 ounces
3. 44 pounds, 12 ounces
4. A. 1,729 ounces   B. $108\frac{1}{16}$ pounds
5. 5 cups

Day 3
1. A. Steven   B. Caroline
2. Rose and Sharon
3. 30
4. A. 6 pounds and 8 ounces
B. 1 pound and 14 ounces
5. 8.548 km

Day 4
1. A. giraffe   B. 81 cm or 810 mm
2. puppy
3. A. kid   B. 13 ounces
4. 12 pounds, 6 ounces
5. A. marker   B. 9 mm
6. A. 0.835   B. 8.35   C. 83.5

Day 5
1. A. bell tower   B. 15 inches or 1 foot and 3 inches
2. A. Priscilla   B. 0.194 km
3. 42
4. 640
5. A. grapefruit   B. $1\frac{5}{8}$ pounds or 26 ounces
6. A. 75 pounds and 11 ounces
B. 16 pounds and 11 ounces

Week 15

Day 1
1. 12
2. 6 inches
3. $\frac{1}{2}$ inch
4. $7\frac{3}{4}$
5. 6
6. 5

Day 2
1. 1
2. $6\frac{1}{4}$
3. $\frac{5}{8}$
4. 44
5. 23
6. 11

Day 3
1. 23
2. $2\frac{3}{10}$ or 2.3
3. 10
4. $1\frac{1}{2}$ meters
5. $16\frac{1}{2}$ meters
6. $1\frac{13}{20}$ meters

Day 4
1. 5 feet
2. $\frac{3}{4}$ feet
3. 0
4. 12.49
5. A. two thousand, seven hundred sixty-five and nine tenths   B. 2,765.9
6. The value of expression A is 3 less than the value of Expression B or the value of Expression B is 3 more than the value of Expression A.

Day 5
1. 15
2. 9 cups
3. 21 cups
4. $\frac{1}{10}$ - foot^2
5. 3
6. two ones

Week 16

Day 1
1. 480
2. 20
3. C
4. A and B
5. 140
6. 36

Day 2
1. 30
2. 514
3. 280
4. 10
5. A. dog   B. 58 oz or $3\frac{5}{8}$ pounds
6. A. $C = 11 \div 8$ B. $1\frac{3}{8}$ pounds

Day 3
1. 540
2. B
3. A and D
4. 60
5. 112
6. A. $P = 6 \div \frac{1}{3}$ B. 18

Day 4
1. 815 units^3
2. 150
3. 462
4. 32
5. Answers will vary but may include that the product is less than either factor because both factors are < 1 so the product will be less than any number being multiplied by a fraction less than 1.
6. 432

Day 5
1. 112
2. B
3. A
4. 192
5. C and D
6. 1,080

Week 17

Day 1
1. 30 in^3
2. 60 in^3
3. 180 in^3
4. 30 in^3
5. $306\frac{3}{19}$
6. 75 feet^3

Day 2
1. 150 in^3
2. 100 in^3
3. 600 in^3
4. 24 cm^3
5. 32 cm^3
6. $\frac{1}{9}$ of a gallon

Day 3
1. 30 yd^3
2. 210 yd^3
3. 6 yd^3
4. 48 mm or 4.8 cm
5. 16,000
6. 267

Day 4
1. 72 m^3
2. 18 m^3
3. 144 m^3
4. 3,516.02
5. 125 mm^3
6. A. $B = 4,242 \div 42$ B. 101

Day 5
1. 80 in^3
2. 240 in^3
3. 48 in^3
4. 56
5. 280 m^3

Week 18

Day 1
1. 336 cm^3
2. 2,352 ft^3
3. $\frac{4}{15} \times 5 = 1\frac{1}{3}$
4. 1,728 ft^3
5. 36 m^3
6. 6

Day 2
1. 756 ft^3
2. 420 ft^3
3. 1,176 ft^3
4. 60 ft^3
5. 20 ft^3
6. 7 hours

Day 3
1. 6,555 in^3
2. 301 in^3
3. The volume of Figure A is 118 yd^3 more than the volume of Figure B or the volume of Figure B is 118 yd^3 less than the volume of Figure A.
4. $\frac{8}{35}$ m^2
5. She did not line up the decimals so that the place values were aligned.
6. $\frac{1}{3}$

Day 4
1. 2 inches × 5 inches
2. 7 × 13
3. 2,912 in^3
4. 720 m^3
5. 2,160 m^3
6. 90

Day 5
1. 440 cm^3
2. 1,430 cm^3
3. 1,870 cm^3
4. A. A   B. C
5. D

Week 19

Day 1
1. (2, 3)
2. 1
3. A and D
4. B and C
5. C
6. Answers may vary but should include something similar to: $\frac{4}{4} = 1$ and any number multiplied by 1 is equal to the original number so 1 × 10 = 10.

Day 2
1. (0, 0)
2. (2, 3)
3. A and D
4. C
5. 5
6. 14,080 and 0.01408

Day 3
1. (2, 7)
2. 5
3. They have the same y-coordinate
4. Aspen
5. $53\frac{11}{15}$

Day 4
1. (2, 4)
2. A. Duffers   B. Ava's and BananaRama
3. A. x-coordinate   B. 5
4. 254,968
5. 6 months

Day 5
1. Bernardo's and DownTown
2. (4, 4)
3. Axed
4. Chime
5. 35 mm^3

Week 20

Day 1
1. quadrilateral
2. quadrilateral, parallelogram
3. C
4. A and D
5. pentagon
6. All rectangles have 4 right angles, 2 pairs of opposite sides that are equal and 2 pairs of parallel lines

Day 2
1. B, C and D
2. A, B and C
3. parallelogram and rhombus
4. A
5. A. An isosceles triangle is a shape that has 3 sides and 2 of those sides are equal in length.
B. Shapes will vary but should have 3 total sides with 2 sides that are equal.
6. octagon

Day 3
1. rhombus
2. trapezoid
3. rectangle
4. square or rhombus
5. equilateral triangle
6. $18\frac{7}{10}$

Day 4
1. quadrilateral
2. rhombus
3. trapezoid
4. A. Parallelograms have 4 sides and opposite sides are equal and parallel.
B. Squares, rectangles and rhombuses are parallelograms.
5. 64
6. A. bag of peaches   B. 1 pound (or 16 oz)

Day 5
1. right triangle
2. A
3. A
4. quadrilaterals
5. A. Rectangles and squares both have right angles and opposite sides that are equal and parallel.
B. Squares have 4 equal sides, rectangles do not.
6. $9\frac{3}{8}$

CHALLENGE QUESTION

Week 1
A. 1,368,940 and 136,894,000
B. 136.894 and 1.36894

Week 2
A. eight million, nine hundred seven thousand, one hundred forty-five and twenty-six hundredths
B. $(8 \times 1{,}000{,}000) + (9 \times 100{,}000) + (7 \times 1{,}000) + (1 \times 100) + (4 \times 10) + (5 \times 1) + \left(2 \times \frac{1}{10}\right) + \left(6 \times \frac{1}{100}\right)$

Week 3
$5619.0 + 5{,}600 = 11{,}219$

Week 4
85.81

Week 5
$(2 \times 6) + 8$ or $8 + (2 \times 6)$

Week 6
$4 \times (5 + 12)$ or $(5 + 12) \times 4$

Week 7
$14\frac{1}{8}$

Week 8
Both addends are larger than $\frac{1}{5}$ so when they are added together, the sum should also be larger than $\frac{1}{5}$.

Week 9
7 km

Week 10
$\frac{5}{12}$ m²

Week 11
Answers should include that the product would be greater than $\frac{3}{5}$ but less than 4.

Week 12
Janna spent $4\frac{2}{3}$ hours and Kit spent $\frac{7}{9}$ hours.

Week 13
A. $C = \frac{1}{6} \div 4$
B. $\frac{1}{24}$

Week 14
$25.44

Week 15
7,100 m or 7.1 km

Week 16
If the 3 numbers given by the student equal 180 when multiplied, the answer is correct. Some examples: $2 \times 3 \times 30$ or $5 \times 4 \times 9$

Week 17
121 cubic meters

Week 18
3,409 in³

Week 19
(2, 9)

Week 20
Both shapes are quadrilaterals that have 2 pairs of parallel lines, opposite sides are equal, and opposite angles are equal.

ASSESSMENT

1. (4, 6)

2. Avocados and donuts

3. Bread

4. 112 cm³

5. 336 cm³

6. Both of them are quadrilaterals, rectangles and parallelograms.

7. The train traveled 1,035 meters farther.

8. Answers may vary and could include:
a. $\frac{2}{3} > \frac{2}{12}$ so the answer should be something more than $\frac{2}{12}$.
b. $\frac{1}{4} > \frac{2}{12}$ so the answer should be something more than $\frac{2}{12}$.

9. The decimal point moves 5 places to the right.

10. three hundredths

11. 5

12. $18\frac{3}{4}$

13. 9 and 10

14. $20

15. $45

16. hundred thousands

17. They both are quadrilaterals (and have 1 pair of parallel lines).

18. $\frac{1}{2}$ cm²

19. 56

20. 19.5 m³

21. 152

22. 14,306.07

23. 30 in³

24. 60 in³

25. 90 in³

26. 1,251

27. $9 \times (3 + 10)$

28. 48

29. $91\frac{1}{2}$

30. 12.10

31. A

32. D

33. B

34. C

35. D

36. C

37. D

38. B

39. A

40. B

41. D

42. D

43. B

44. A

45. C

46. A

47. B

48. B

50654850R00083

Made in the USA
San Bernardino, CA
29 June 2017